KILLING AUNTIE
& other work

(B) *editions*

01 / Erik Houston *The White Room*

02 / Jennie Walker *24 for 3*

03 / Jack Robinson *Days and Nights in W12*

04 / Stefan Grabiński *In Sarah's House*
   (translated by Wiesiek Powaga)

05 / *Saxon* screenplay by Greg Loftin

06 / Gert Hofmann *Lichtenberg & The Little Flower Girl*
   (translated by Michael Hofmann)

07 / Francis Ponge *Unfinished Ode to Mud*
   (translated by Beverley Bie Brahic)

08 / Elise Valmorbida *The TV President*

09 / J. O. Morgan *Natural Mechanical*

10 / Christopher Reid *The Song of Lunch*

11 / Jack Robinson *Recessional*

12 / Andrzej Bursa *Killing Auntie and Other Work*
   (translated by Wiesiek Powaga)

13/ Nicky Singer *Knight Crew*

www.cbeditions.com

Andrzej Bursa

KILLING AUNTIE

& other work

translated by
Wiesiek Powaga

CB editions

First published in 2009
by CB editions
146 Percy Road London W12 9QL
www.cbeditions.com

Printed in England by Primary Colours, London W3 8DH

ISBN 978–0–9557285–8–7

This publication has been subsidised by
Instytut Książki – the ©POLAND Translation Programme

INSTYTUT KSIĄŻKI

©POLAND

Contents

Fairy Tale 1

Preface 3

I'd Like to Be a Poet 12

Poet 13

Amoeba 14

Horse 15

Summons 16

'You know all my tricks' 18

To Myself Dead 19

'Doctor C the rich man' 20

Thanksgiving Prayer (with a grudge) 21

Auschwitz – Excursion 22

Talking to a Wise Man 23

Chess 24

Of Various Ways to Humiliate Short Guys 25

Complaint 26

Phantom Warsaw 28

Roughneck Syllogism 29

In Praise of Begging 30

The Carbuncle; or, Theatre of Horrors 33

The Song of a Sewing Machine 37

Freemason 38

Rustic Dialogue; or, Socialistic Faraway 40

The Dragon 42

Prophet 48

My Day 49

Love 50

Function of Poetry 51

Women's War 52

Thirteen-year-old 54

Saint Joseph 55

from Children's Fun and Games 56

Jazz Song 57

'I know those little streets' 58

Killing Auntie 59

Eleven-year-old in Love 148

Fairy Tale

Once upon a time he got on the wrong side of the Emperor. The Emperor wanted to order his head chopped off but had no time. So he said:

'Please be so good to report to my office and remind me that you should have your head chopped off.'

So he reported. At first he took it badly. He thought a lot about the transience of existence and limits of individual freedom and dependence on the whims of some stupid despot. But then he got on with it. For the clerks he was a real pain in the neck. Mountains of work, petitioners fainting in the queues and he:

'Hello. The Emperor asked me to remind you that I should have my head chopped off. Goodbye.'

And so on, every hour.

Punctually two minutes before twelve he would run out of the Ministerial Café (he wouldn't be seen anywhere else) to quickly rattle off his formula. Every Saturday at eleven in the night, slightly swaying on his feet after a bottle downed at the Ambassador's (he wouldn't drink anywhere else), he would turn up at the office and mumble out:

'M'peror ordered . . . you know . . . mmm . . . I should have my head chopped off.'

At four in the morning he would drag himself off his camp bed stretched out in the corridor (he wouldn't sleep anywhere else) and in sleepy voice would wake the desk clerk:

'The Emperor ordered . . .' and so on.

Twenty years passed. One day in the office he bumped into the Emperor, who was an old man now.

'What's this man doing here?' asked the Emperor.

'He reports here because His Imperial Highness is to chop his head off,' answered the secretary.

'Chop it off then,' bridled the Emperor.

So they did.

End of fairy tale.

Preface

Andrzej Bursa (1932–1957), poet, writer, playwright, journalist, despite his short life and relatively small literary output created a diverse and original body of work which secured him a unique place in Poland's postwar literature. He made his poetic debut in 1954 in a Kraków newspaper, but the bulk of his work was written between 1955 and 1957 and was never published in his lifetime.

The first volume of his poetry, published in 1958, consisted mostly of material the publisher had previously rejected. A fuller collection of his work, including prose and drama, edited by Stanisław Stanuch and published in 1969, was followed by further two editions and by a collection of poetry in 1977.

Andrzej Bursa was born into a family of Polish pre-war intelligentsia with long artistic traditions, especially in music. His wartime childhood and the tragic deaths of his aunts in Auschwitz affected him deeply and left him with an indelible if carefully masked scar. His education began with the outbreak of the war and continued at the secret educational courses run by the Polish underground. After the war, following his parents' divorce, he stayed with his mother and sister in Kraków, while his father, a school inspector committed to the cause of the new regime, moved to Wrocław and then to Warsaw. Young Bursa continued his education in a Kraków gymnasium, where he first tried his hand writing for a school paper. He failed his matriculation exam in 1950, but he passed it a year later as an external student. He enrolled at an art college (where he met his future wife, Ludwika), then moved to the Yagiellonean University to study first journalism

3

and then Bulgarian. The birth of his son in 1952 forced him to abandon education and in 1954 Bursa began full time work at a Kraków paper, starting at the news desk and graduating to reportage and cultural events. By 1957 he had published over thirty poems in various papers and literary magazines, and placed a proposal for his first volume of poetry with a major Polish publisher. At the point of death he left in his drawer about a hundred poems, several plays and a good dozen prose pieces, including a novel.

He died suddenly and unexpectedly of natural causes (congenital malformation of the aorta) weeks after receiving a rejection letter from a publisher. This circumstance, as well as the tone of his writing, which by then had begun to be better known in the artistic circles of young Kraków, gave rise to a legend of a young poet rebel who, unable to deal with rejection or bear life under a totalitarian regime, committed suicide. Despite disclaimers published by the family the legend persisted for years; it turned him into a cult figure. This persistent mythologisation was in part a natural reaction to the cruelty and injustice of early death, but it was also a testimony to the power of his voice – the voice of a generation whose childhood was destroyed by the war and whose youth was poisoned by false hopes, and the voice too of later generations of young people: angry, uncompromising in their idealism, stuck between their past and future, creatively destructive, all mixed up and courageous. It is the voice of 'all who once stood terrified before the dead perspective of their youth'.

From the moment I first dipped into the Andrzej *Bursa's Works in Verse and Prose* I felt the warmth of the Holy Anger of Youth radiating from the sparse lines throbbing with indignation and scorn and crying out loud what most people around me only muttered under their breaths. He had the courage to wrestle with form, even if he had to kick it in the crotch. All those lines running off the page, the disdain for capital letters and punctuation, the near-rhymes and the prosaic rhythms of everyday speech, the (to my mind wholly justified) vulgarisms – all those seemingly awkward and indecorous formal flaws somehow jelled into lines which rang out in my head for days.

By then I had already discovered Zbigniew Herbert and his potent, distilled poetry packed into pared-down syntax and laid out in clean, elegant lines. Some of Bursa's poems reminded me of Herbert. They had a similar compressed form, laced with irony and lyricism, and a strong moral flavour. But they were something different. Where Herbert was reaching out for the truth through the classics, Bursa was throwing it out of his pocket by the fistful. He was angry, impatient, ill-mannered, sometimes downright vulgar, yet artful. It all fitted like a glove, and it wasn't a boxing glove. He said what he felt and how he wanted it said. The immediacy of feeling, sometimes violent yet delivered in measured verse and metre, was a revelation.

Despite the pervasive double standards of the school curriculum (Herbert was on both the censor's list and the list of required books), Bursa's work was not read in schools. His absence was perhaps related to the general shortage of everything that plagued mature socialism, forever getting its supply-and-demand knickers in a twist. Be that as it may, I felt I had missed out on something important – I felt cheated. Just like Bursa did.

Bursa made his debut in 1954, a year after Stalin's death, at the beginning of a political thaw which began to relax the communist orthodoxy of social realism. By 1956 the thaw had changed into a tide, and the debut of five poets, among them Białoszewski, Harasymowicz, Herbert and Czycz (who later published an experimental novel *And*, featuring a Bursa-like character) marked a defining moment for Polish post-war poetry. Freed from the straitjacket of the sentimental political propaganda, poetry took on new forms and new themes, and Bursa's writing developed with astonishing speed. As one of his friends recalled (quoted in an article by Krzysztof Cwiklinski, www.dziennik.com): 'Die young? Suits me fine. Imagine, they'll say – so young, so talented, such a promise, such a nice, charming man – that's what they'll say in the obituary – and died so young. When I grow old I'll be an old fart, no one'll give a toss about me, no one'll be sorry. And to die young – so much work off your back . . .' This was of course the foolhardy irreverence of youth talking, but no wonder the legend of a *poet maudit* stuck.

But he was not a *poet maudit*. Compared with the real self-destructive maniacs of Polish poetry such as Wojaczek, he was simply a young ambitious poet, eager to show his work to the world, and he couldn't wait his turn. Impatience is a natural instinct of any young poet; even Herbert, the monument of moral incorruptibility, tried to have his poems published (and succeeded) years before the famous debut of 1956, if under a pseudonym. But while the older poets – Herbert, Różewicz or Białoszewski – generally held back until they were allowed to come out in public with their new, fully matured poetics, Bursa was pushing to the front, wanting to be where the action was.

In 1947, influenced by his father and carried away by youthful enthusiasm, Bursa joined the Polish communist youth organisation (ZWM). His early poem 'Under the Red Flag' was set to music and given a public performance at a conference; apparently this was done without his permission but it shows that the legend of a rebellious James Dean who 'didn't crawl or grovel', like all legends, hides as much as it preserves. In fact he seems to have been just like a lot of his compatriots, swept along by high hopes rising from the ruins; he wasn't alone in taking the promises of the red flag at face value. But it didn't take long before he saw that the face was peeling off the flag. When his ZWM card got washed clean with his trousers he took it for a sign and didn't renew his membership. His motivation for joining the Polish Workers' Party in 1955 may have had much to do with the difficulties facing his young family and his need to secure a better position in the newspaper he worked for.

His published journalistic pieces from this period show a young reporter visiting small towns and attempting to present the country in the process of rebuilding. The most interesting fruit of his travels was the story 'Dragon', which blends the dry style of reportage with a fairy tale in which a young virginal couple, following an ageless local custom, is sacrificed to a dragon. As the feeble old beast is well past its retirement age and the devouring takes place side by side with progress of the new order, on the surface the story can be read as a satire on the deeply rooted conservatism and 'backwardness" of the Polish countryside, well within the directives of the official propaganda. Yet the sparseness of the style and its unblinking naturalism give the story an unexpected universal, even existential depth. Doubtless the young reporter touring small-town Poland witnessed many such horrors; another work deriving from his travels ends: 'You can shove your small towns up your arse!' But once the anger subsided he realised that the aspirations of the new ideology – and the way the new powers went about achieving them – might require more than a couple of four-year plans. This is illustrated in the sur-real (rather than soc-real) sketch 'Rustic Dialogue; or, Socialistic Faraway', which was performed regularly in a popular Kraków cabaret well after the Polish 'real socialism' bit the dust.

The distinguishing mark of Bursa's work is his continuous experiment and struggle with form. But to begin with, to become a poet was a natural ambition for a boy with a keen musical ear and a great facility for rhyming and poetic improvisation. Being 'made a Pole', as he complained in his 'Thanksgiving Prayer (with a grudge)', meant that he had first to square up to the grand tradition of the Polish Romantics. Shaped at the time of Poland's partition and revived with great force during the German occupation, the Romantic tradition conferred on the poet the role of Prophet, Conscience of the Nation and Beacon of Freedom. The surprising number of poems dealing with the role of poet and poetry in Bursa's work, and its sometimes battered form, attests to what a struggle dealing with the Great Tradition must have been. He could look to Mickiewicz, in whose 'Great Improvisation' the Poet vies with God, indifferent to the nation's suffering, for the rule of hearts and comes blasphemously close to comparing Him to the Tsar; this poetic act of rebellion and scornful contempt for the Supreme Authority must have felt close to Bursa's young heart. He could look also to Lautréamont, whose *Songs of Maldoror*, apparently inspired by Mickiewicz's 'Great Improvisation', echoes in Bursa's work not just in 'A Song of the Sewing Machine'. But the condition of 1950s Poland – postwar, post-Auschwitz, and with a rigid, state-enforced censorial – imposed particular challenges. As Stanisław Stanuch, Bursa's champion and the editor of his collected works, remembers: 'For the majority of young people born in 1930s the horror of our time was as commonplace as our daily bread. The more penetrating for being soaked up by souls of six- or seven-year-olds, for whom notions like "execution", "selection", "hostages", "bumping off", "revenge" "soap made of people", "burning corpses in crematoria or in the open air", were part of their everyday conversation. These were not just abstract notions but a way to describe the fate of their closest: fathers, brothers, mothers, sisters, friends.'

Suffering, mutilated bodies, corpses, horror – it all had to be packed in somehow and no wonder an occasional limb plopped out of the suitcase. In his all-out search for the most

8

adequate form it was only a question of time before Bursa turned to theatre, and the extracts from 'The Carbuncle; or, Theatre of Horrors' printed here are another example of his unerring instinct to be where the action was. These were written with his schoolfriend, the actor Jan Guntner, and commissioned and produced by Tadeusz Kantor. Bursa's work includes one complete play (*Count Cagliostro's Animals*), but fragments of two others were produced in his lifetime and many more are marked as work in progress in his archive. His fascination with theatre which focuses on the body as a medium for the intangible points in the direction later fully developed by Kantor and his then assistant Jerzy Grotowski. It could have been his mature form.

The fact that Bursa grew up surrounded by war and Stalinist terror focused his mind in a way that may be difficult to appreciate fifty years later. There are few better examples of how lofty poetic ambitions had to be cruelly readjusted to the new post-Auschwitz world. He was not the only one, and not the first, but while the older, more mature poets had time to adjust, his is a vivid example how the operation was carried out on living tissue. No wonder he sometimes felt like a dead body.

The motif of death and the corpse in Bursa's work certainly contributed to the legend of his suicide, but read from the inside it appears as the chief symbolic device which allowed him to handle the fundamental questions. His most ambitious use of this motif is in the short novel *Killing Auntie*, the manuscript of which lay in Bursa's archive for years before it was patiently pieced together by Stanuch.

The sparseness of the clues as to time and place inside *Killing Auntie* give it the feel of a morality tale. The plot, evolving around the central act of a pointless murder, invites comparisons with Dostoyevsky's *Crime and Punishment*, but while

Raskolnikov's murder of an old usurer had a firm moral – if misguided – justification, Jurek's killing of his good auntie has none: it is practically pointless and potentially self-destructive. It seems that the lack of moral deliberation, indeed of any pre-meditation, and the gratuity of the extreme act that makes it an act of pure evil. But in what sense can evil be pure? And can the gratuity of an act make it evil? The subsequent preoccupation with getting rid of the body in order to avoid being caught and punished becomes almost a game, but something more than a simple catch-me-if-you-can game: it's a game played as much with the corpse itself as against the catchers, reminiscent of Daniil Kharms's 'Old Woman'. The surprising end suggests it was a carefully set up test of the validity of a moral code, and a scrupulous – one might say a surgical – examination of the tangibility of guilt.

The vague timelessness of *Killing Auntie*, combined with a realistic setting and naturalistic descriptions, also suggest parallels with Kafka. Both Dostoyevsky and Kafka were admitted into the official canon in Poland through the back door of new translations only after Stalin's death. Kafka especially must have posed problems for a new totalitarian regime, and was no doubt high on Bursa's personal list of required reading. Much of his prose ('Summons' and 'Women's War' are examples) has a strong Kafkaesque flavour; what makes this different from a simple youthful influence is the direct connection to his childhood experience, as in the case of 'Horse' – a brutally beaten horse (which appears as a symbol of pointless human cruelty also in Dostoyevsky, Nietzsche and Mayakovski) is presented as an 'accumulator of suffering' in the manner of Kafka, but its description derives from an image imprinted on the boy's mind on visits to the coal depot with his father during the war.

Killing Auntie also testifies to the softer, sensitive side of Bursa that is often obscured by the legend of the rebellious, uncompromising, sharp-tongued poet. His aggression and contempt were at least in part a cultivated, protective veneer. His angry poetic gestures were rooted in a deep emotional trauma resulting from the explosive collision of innocent childhood and brave youth with real world, in his case the world of horror and guilt. He was young, still searching for the right form, resonating with different influences and inspiration; but his anger, linked with an unresolved sense of guilt, childish perhaps but whose sense is universally human, became the mainspring of his creative mechanics, and the interplay between childlike sensitivity and a callous skin of disdain and derision is the key to understanding Bursa's writing.

Final word about aunties: I first read Bursa when I was seventeen, a long-haired rebel in a school run according to the drab rules of 'mature socialism' in 1970s Poland, and immediately felt I had found a kindred spirit. His book was passed to me by an old lady, the school librarian, who must have felt a soft spot for a skinny youth enquiring naively about books outside the required reading list. Hats off to old wise school librarians, those kindly aunties ready to sacrifice themselves on the pyre of youth.

W.P.

I'd Like to Be a Poet

I'd like to be a poet
'Cause poet's life is great
Always in a lovely sweater
Desert boots walking a setter
And he doesn't have a care

I'd like to be a poet
For a poet's life is heaven
For a poet has four wives
Naturally long divorced
And I do like women

I'd like to be a poet
I may even get a grant
If I get to know the right people
I won't have to get up early
Mornings can be nippy

For a poet's life's a dream
Not for him the office hours
And to hell with discipline
Only music and a girlfriend
And counting lucky stars

And erring and counting
And starting from the beginning
On earth in trees and sky
Looking for a shade of meaning

And getting mad and worried
Because it's still not right
And always searching and always stuck
I hate being a poet

Poet

A poet suffers for the millions
From 10 to 1.30
At 11 his bladder is full
He goes out
Unzips his flies
Zips up his flies
Returns to his desk
Clears his throat
And again
Suffers for the millions

Amoeba

Children are nicer than grown-ups
Animals are nicer than children
You are telling me that thinking
This way I have to come to the conclusion
That the nicest thing is an amoeba

So what?

Amoeba is nicer to me
Than you
Bastard!

Horse

Have you seen, ladies and gentlemen, a horse standing stock still in the clay yard, surrounded by empty stables and farm buildings? Such a horse, dug into the ground, has no hauling value, it's useless. Exposed to rain, freezing cold and heat, flogged, tormented by horseflies – it suffers. That's its function.

The horse's hide, full of blisters and puss, is a veritable map of pain, full of geographic paradoxes and surprises. For instance, that apparently horrible, massive blister is nothing but a dead scrap of skin, while the little wound in the crotch, invisible to a cursory glance, is a practically inexhaustible seam of pain.

Because, as we pointed out earlier, the horse's legs are dug into the ground, he cannot move, and so every effort he makes to do so under the whip only multiplies his suffering. So, the horse is an accumulator of suffering. It automatically, through its own effort, self-charges with pain. Its reserves are so great it can be shared out among several families.

But show me, ladies and gentlemen, who is today looking for suffering?

Nevertheless, the horse is indispensable and it's hard to imagine how the world can function without it.

Summons

From time to time one of the men in our town receives a summons to report to a certain address in order to have his right hand cut off. The summons contains only one line written clearly in ink on a piece of cheap grid paper. At the bottom there are some black blots; it's impossible to tell if they are just splashed ink or a feebly pressed stamp. None of the summoned men could ever determine with any certitude that it was not a stamp.

The date given is usually some twenty to thirty-five days from receiving the summons. Usually the letter arrives in early May so that the date falls at the beginning of summer holidays.

On the appointed day the summoned man slips out of his home under some excuse and goes to the given address with his right hand clenched into a fist inside his pocket and pressed into the crotch. The address is a small pretentious townhouse, in fact little more than a adjunct of the much bigger Social Security office. On the steps one can often see doctors and nurses who use it as a shortcut to the café on the corner. In the corridor on the first floor the man hands the paper to a neatly dressed young woman. It hasn't happened yet that anyone is seen to straight away. The young woman asks the man to kindly wait two, three hours or return in a few days' time. In front of the house there is an overgrown green square. That's where all the summoned men wait.

The operation takes place in a cosy room not unlike a dentist's surgery. On the ceiling and one of the walls there is mounted a powerful, complex machine, a dozen or so circular blades with very thin and very sharp edges, and a few lamps. The operation is carried out by an old frail doctor and his assistant, a girl in her early twenties. In fact it she is who really matters. With a truly admirable skill she staunches the blood gushing out the moment the sharp blade severs the hand. Usually the patient faints and wakes up some twelve hours later, a little weak but alert, and with one hand less.

It hasn't happened yet that a summoned man fails to report for the treatment.

Although, once, a summoned sixth-former left the town on the eve of his operation and for a few days wandered aimlessly the neighbouring fields and woods. He was eventually found in a haystack, mad, and transported to a mental hospital. He is there to this day. He has saved his hand but lost his mind, for ever.

*

. . . you know all my tricks, and I know yours;
we are wasting our time.
– Roger Vailland

You know all my tricks
my life
you know when I start scratching screaming and
    thrashing about
you know the obstinacy of my struggles
and the numb tasteless senseless exhaustion
then you poison my dreams with nightmares
denying any possibility of refuge
I know your just desserts
which I accept with eager gratitude
which make me retch in convulsions
I'm used to your cruelty
I've learnt to laugh at my own cadaver
(you know it well this trick of mine)
we are bored of each other my life
                my enemy

and now you've fixed my jaw with a glitter of pain
to stop me yawning

To Myself Dead

When I was dead for good
I turned to my wife and whispered
I'm sorry darling but
I need to pop out, and left her

Just as my spectre walked out
It bumped into a girl I knew
I'm dead you know, it's cool
But my death was showing through

My mates sat around me talking
Smoking, sweaty, breathing air
What's up, you really dead?
Come on Andy hang in there . . .

Down the streets that barred my world
Then to the station across the tracks
I wandered silent growing cold
Where I roamed before as a living corpse

Following footsteps of wasted time
Of boring yearning empty youth
Struck in the living heart with a knife
Kissed on the mouth
                    with a knuckleduster

*

Doctor C the rich man and a miracle worker
and all thanks to his hard work
(difficult childhood hard work
high school hard work
medical school hard work
a villa comfortable as cloud nine
and two cars more beautiful than stars
also thanks to his hard work)
he has a collection of torsos
those losers without arms and legs
he has 22 of them
that is two elevens
so he says
right boys today we will learn to play football
– but we have no legs whine the slackers
– rubbish says the doctor
I've made it thanks to hard work
thanks to hard work you can work miracles
and he winks at the nurse the ex-sergeant

Six months they trained in the sanatorium behind the
    barbed wire

I don't know if they grew legs
I don't know how it came about
but I did see their springtime match
and the boys were kicking the ball
like there was no tomorrow

Thanksgiving Prayer (with a grudge)

You didn't make me blind
Thank you O Lord

You didn't give me a hump
Thank you O Lord

You didn't make my father an alkie
Thank you O Lord

You didn't give me water on the brain
Thank you O Lord

You didn't make me limp a dwarf an epileptic
    hermaphrodite a horse moss or something
From your flora or fauna
Thank you O Lord

But why did you make me a Pole?

Auschwitz – Excursion

Inside Auschwitz's barren rib-cage
Through which the setting sun flowed
Like blood
We journalists wandered around looking
Into the black holes of crematoria
And the innards of huts
Like into Santa's grotto
Excuse me, why there is no graffiti on the walls?

Right . . . graffiti
The living annals
Mother!
Or: Poland!
Or: Fight on!
There's nothing . . . painted over.
Squeaking our new spring shoes
Rustling our trench coats
We trod the ground
Where once each step was searing pain
We focused our lenses
Blasphemously objective
We froze in poses
Understanding nothing

Distanced by aeons
By ten years of glorious socialism
From the ashes of fathers of our mates

[1955]

Talking to a Wise Man

The moment he opened his mouth the demons started coming out of me. Pretending I was listening to his arguments (highly convincing, no doubt) I watched my demons, whose number grew commensurably with his words, his madness and his exhaustion. Until their number grew to 40, 000. They took up all the oxygen in the room. Then he had enough. He grew pale and stammered out:

'Could you open the window please?'

I didn't budge. He staggered towards the window and finding it wide open he turned around and gave me a questioning look.

I nodded.

Wow, how the air swished in the room! How my demons laughed!

When he went crrraaaah . . . down from the fourth floor . . . Crrraaaah . . .! Down.

Chess

A friend of mine, thick and malicious like a hundred mules, brings his chessboard and asks: You playing? Ha ha, I know this trick of his. I know that as the game progresses my pieces heat up white-hot. By the third move they will sizzle and burn the fingertips black. But I'm playing, of course I'm playing. Check, garde, check. I lose two knights and a rook, my fingers smoke like factory chimneys. I try to push the pawn with my fingernail, but met with my partner's ironic stare I give up. The partner is generous too – You'll lose the queen, he warns me – take it back. And so prolongs my torment.

When he takes my second rook, I consider surrender, to stop that idiotic torture. But then he lowers his guard. So, face twisted with pain, I make another wrong move. Hee hee – chuckles my stupid friend – That's life, innit. That's his favourite joke. It's endgame. With the last blister I move the king into inescapable mate.

My friend titters and sweeps the chess pieces.

Then I cry – Now revenge!

Of Various Ways to Humiliate Short Guys

At a party call him out to another room and offer him a cigarette. When the shorty courteously offers you a lit match, take it out of his hand, grab him by the collar and hold him over the fire. At first he will protest. Flick him on the nose and warn him that if he continues making so much noise his girlfriend, now dancing with one of your friends, may come in. Soon shorty will shut up and stop wriggling, only his moist eyes will be glistening in the dark room. Then put him down on his feet. When the shorty tries to sneak out of the room give him a mighty slap on the face. He will stop in his tracks and flutter his eyelids. Then whack him again.

Shorty will start offering you now the left, now the right cheek, begging you all the while with half-gestures and imploring glances to keep your slaps quiet or his girlfriend might hear and come in. This is the funniest bit, especially if the shorty starts trotting on the spot with his burnt feet. Now you can let him go. See how he runs off to his girlfriend. You may want to send him an ironic look but try to avoid it. It's a cheap effect.

Similarly, just like with the shorties, you can deal with hunchbacks. But here you have to be careful. This type, when driven to despair, can kill.

Complaint

Dear Minister of Justice, sir,
You offend me.
I do not know you but I have seen your photo in a
    newspaper
and I feel deeply offended,
unfortunately not just by you.
Majority of governmental and social institutions
are a personal affront to me,
most of citizens in our country
are insults aimed directly at me.
Really sometimes I wonder who would bother to build
    this preposterous machinery
with architecture, army, law and crime
only to
torment me
personally.
Even on the street corner they installed a blind man
    just to drive me mad
And if you were to send me a parcel with a letter:
    Dear Mr Bursa,
    You are a pretty clever boy
    Here is a pair of shoes size 42
    Signed: Mankind
    Government
    Or possibly: World Council
But no,
This is waste of money for you.
And for creating all those ideologies and apostles
    of which each and every one has to have at least
    twenty pairs of shoes (including kid leather tops)
    just to spite me, for this you'll always find a few
    pennies.

Sir,

All in all I don't blame you. You are just one of those bitter pills they secretly drop (your silly jokes) into my morning coffee. I'll digest you too.

But law – what does the law have to say about it?

Phantom Warsaw

When I got off the train in Warsaw
I saw through the whole act
This was not Warsaw at all
(just like the train was not a train)
but one big phantom
one monumental con-machine
cheap elaborate joke
at my expense
at every turn I discover
the phoniness
time and time again I see
the hardboard showing through fake facades
the wise guy I'm talking to in his office
is not all there too
simply a torso screwed into the chair
he can get 'upset'
but he can't 'rise' at all
they thought I wouldn't notice lack of feet under the chair
cartoon cut-out profiles
proletariat stuffed with sawdust
all flash but no flesh
everything old hat
makes you laugh
except at night
through the window
it haunts you
the Phantom Warsaw

Roughneck Syllogism

You won't get anything pretty for free
Sunset is free
So it's not pretty
But to puke all over the loo in a posh joint
You have to pay for the vodka first
Ergo
The loo in a disco is pretty
And sunset's not

But I'm telling you it's all humbug

I've seen the sunset
And the loo in a nightclub

Same difference

In Praise of Begging

So you think one shouldn't give them any money
that most of them can work
work . . . that's a good one
so if that barnacled one with Tolstoy's head
swung the shovel in a ditch
and that old man with a fake wound kept watch
by the shovel storehouse
and that witch (you were a child once) weeded beets
you would be satisfied

they do work and how
for any small change they can deliver pure wholesome
    emotion any time
they don't eat wooden bread
they don't pretend (now that's a word worth your
    culture) to be dead
like you do in your theatres
they offer their whole bodies to freezing cold and
    scorching heat and pouring rain
with every gesture word and louse on their collar
to achieve their effect they have to follow strictly the
    regime
of life-given rules
sleep on park benches railway stations miss their trains
    and
get drunk
and despite the fact that their death and bread are real
their art is in no way naturalistic
they achieve that fullness of a universal law which can
    only be
dreamt of by your academic mannequins
they are avant-garde through and through

even though their art is old as the world
modern artists should take lessons from them and the
    clever ones do
on the Kraków-Przemysl train a white-sticked blind
    man opened the compartment door
and you know what all those numb comfort-seeking
    bodies on the bench had to face
a problem which your dramatic art couldn't see if it
    banged it on the head
it's you who do fuck all
what have you done today mr writer
what is your occupation mr dj
how much do they pay you kitchen goddess
who pays for your agent's vodka
(they never fail to make me laugh when they complain
    that beggars drink)
look at yourselves!

that dwarf 4 feet 2
shoe size 45
plays on the accordion
with hands like boughs (three beetrooty offshoots at
    the end of each)
a church hymn
combining Grand Guignol
with mystery play and
he does it with style

or that one thrashing around in a fit
(for you the ballet is still a dignified romp isn't it)
a member of the intelligentsia in reduced
    circumstances (what a make-up!)
says he's just been released
totally innocent facing now a moral conflict
can't bring himself to ask note the gesture

how he puts away that fiver

a sweet old man with a doggy on a carpet
to keep the poor thing warm
a mad lady in a man's hat
father grieving after losing
three sons all heroes

they may be actors of one role
but they do it to perfection
do not think I'm fraternising with lumpenproletariat
the beggars are mostly smelly fools
they put me off as much
as you the artists
but their art is more
to my taste

The Carbuncle; or, Theatre of Horrors

[*written with Jan Guntner*]

Two Soldiers

Two soldiers, one unarmed, the other armed with a machine gun. The armed one keeps his gun trained on the unarmed one. Tension. After a while the tension subsides. After a further while nothing much is happening. They even begin to smile at each other. The unarmed one slowly lowers one of his hands and puts it in his pocket. A shot. The unarmed one, falling down, yanks his hand out of the pocket. From the dead hand roll out cigarettes.

The Kitchen

A bustling, merry washerwoman is washing a bedsheet. On the fire boils a big cauldron. The washerwoman wrings the sheet out and hangs it up. Then she comes up to the cauldron, stirs it energetically, takes it off the fire and fishes out a newborn babe. The hanging bedsheet turns red.

The Door

Hygienically clean white door. A man approaches. His clothes are poor. Timidly, he knocks on the door, puts his hand on the door handle. The door stays shut. The man tries again. He is persistent, and clumsy; the door is consistent, and wise. The man's anger grows; he begins to bang his fists on the door and scratch it. As the man weakens and despairs, the door grows active, becoming aggressive and ruthless. It goes into attack. It injures the man's forehead, slams on his fingers. The fight grows apace, faster and faster. At last the man falls by the door. The door remains on the battlefield white, hygienic, unassailable.

A Wounded Girl

Two shadows. Naked Girl and Lover (young, handsome, smartly dressed). Lover gently and attentively strokes Girl's face. Then, with the same gesture, he strokes her breasts, shoulders, hips. The screen and the shadows disappear. Girl stands naked. The parts of her body touched by Lover are deep bleeding wounds.

The Apothecary

Inside the chemist's. Behind the counter, with rows of jars behind him, stands the Philosophical Apothecary. He wears the clothes of a wizard. Against the glassed door stands a girl, his daughter. The girl has her back to us and we do not know she is crying.

From afar comes the sound of hobnailed boots. It may be group of soldiers. A sound of a penny whistle. The Apothecary listens intently to the fading sound of marching boots.

The night comes suddenly. The jars filled with colourful potions glisten and flicker with reflected light. Through the glass door one can see the sky criss-crossed with anti-aircraft searchlights. The girl turns around. Down her tired but indifferent face trickle tears. She slowly walks up to the Apothecary. He strokes her good-naturedly; he wants to comfort her.

The girl calms down. The Apothecary turns to one of the shelves and takes down a big jar with poison. He is quietly happy. He hands the jar to the girl; she receives it from him as if it were something precious. She cradles the jar in her arms. She is calm now. Her face lights up with a smile.

Cats

On the gynaecological chair lies a girl. Her naked legs spread wide apart are raised; her head thrown back. Between the legs stands a doctor in a white coat. The doctor has six arms. All the arms are working. Soft, fluid movements. The quiet whirr of a machine. With graceful movement the doctor pulls out two kittens. He throws them into a bucket. When the girl is left alone a gentleman appears in a top hat and a frock, with a bouquet of flowers. He lays the flowers at her head. He takes off his hat. He has cat's ears.

The Guillotine

The guillotine. Two sans-culottes, dressed in overalls, Wellington boots and Phrygian caps, busy at work. Strong wind.

First sans-culotte: In the name of the Convention, by will of the People.

The blade falls.

Second sans-culotte (lifting the severed head): Queen Marie Antoinette Thérèse Mosel, Sovereign of Franconia, Princess of Aragon, Albion, Luxembourg, Aquitaine, the lady of Two Tulips and Seven Suns.

Warbling drums. A roar of the crowd.

First sans-culotte: In the name of the Convention, by will of the People.

Blade falls.

Second sans-culotte (lifting the severed head): Marquis Sebastian Jacob Erasm de Parde, lord of 700 vineyards and 300 farms.

Warbling drums. Roar of the crowd.

First sans-culotte: In the name of the Convention, by will of the People.

Blade falls.

Second sans-culotte (lifting the severed head): Bishop Grand Cochon, pastor of a hundred parishes, lord of 4,000 acres and of 3,000 absolutions.

Warbling drums. A roar of the crowd.

First sans-culotte: In the name of the Convention, by will of the People.

Blade falls.

Second sans-culotte takes out of the basket a freshly cut rose. Holds it in his hand, surprised. Says: A rose. Lifts it up in the air like he did a severed head before.

Warbling drums. A roar of the crowd, as before.

The Song of a Sewing Machine

In the city's tarmac veins autumn's blood coagulates,
Evening tightens the noose, dusk thickens with sighs.
Nothing ever comes back, all is beyond change and fades
Like mist drifting by.

Days flicker like pale fingers, busy and diligent,
While nights flare up on the ruins of dreams.
May blooms only once but its scent can burn
the heart at whim.

O fleeting, perfumed May, charm of the streets,
You bleed in jasmine's sticky clasp from roses fair
When twilight seeps through heavy skies and fills
The courtyard well.

Days are like fingers, nights like ruins steep,
The pricked heart glistens in trickles of blood
And all is beyond change for even in sleep
It aches, it bleeds . . . my heart.

Freemason

No one would ever suspect that our quiet, mild-mannered clerk, Stephan, might be a freemason. And yet it turned out to be true. The news brought by one of our colleagues spread through the office like a wildfire and on the second day reached even the director. Director's reaction fell somewhere between 'nah . . .' and 'hm . . .' but then after hours he sat alone in his office for a long time drumming fingers on his desk.

On the third day the manager B, a stout and impulsive man, out of the blue turned to Stephan:

'Have you seen my square and compasses? Don't know where I put them . . .'

Stephan looked confused. For as long as he could remember no one used a square or a pair of compasses in the office. He stuttered out – 'N-no . . . ha-haven't seen any . . .' – and quickly lowered his head over the papers. A triumphant whisper swept through the office. There was no doubt now. That same day Director decided to investigate the matter himself.

Director had been with us only a few months, having been transferred from a recently closed institution where the preferred management tool was the psychological method. It was with this method that he decided to solve the mystery. He summoned Stephan to his office and without any pussyfooting employed the method.

'So how are we today, Stephan?'

Stephan flushed red, started mumbling something, tried to smile. All that did not escape the Director's sharp eye.

'Because you know,' Director pressed on, 'life is terribly boring. Terribly boring. What would you say to a weekend of shooting? I have a lovely lodge . . .'

Stephan smiled ever so evasively. He began to make suspicious movements with his body and rub his hands. Director knew he had him.

'You will be very comfortable in the lodge, won't you?' he said. 'In the lodge, you know . . . in the lodge,' he repeated with emphasis.

'But . . . of course,' mumbled out Stephan and then suddenly Director rose to his feet and stretched out his hand.

'Very well, that's all for now. Please go back to your work.'

Before long Stephan was summoned to Director's office again. This time Director told him that for reasons which are too numerous to list here his services were no longer required.

When the news of the Director's decision got out no one felt sorry for the quiet mild-mannered clerk. People don't like freemasons.

Rustic Dialogue; or, Socialistic Faraway

DRAMATIS PERSONAE:
PEASANT A
PEASANT B

PEASANT A: Think what ye will, Pigarso's all right, Pinnyon's all right, but methinks them tachists they are no good.

PEASANT B: Aye, you'd know, eh? You rattle yer trap like an old bucket . . .

PEASANT A: Apropos Bucket – d'you know that play of his? Fine piece, fine piece. *Pioor* existentialism.

PEASANT B: Are you putting it on at the club?

PEASANT A: That I don't know. We 'ave three parties in the village. Our village head bangs on and on about that Giro . . . What you call him, Giro-do, or that other An-hole . . .

PEASANT B: An-hooy?

PEASANT A: That's it – Anhooy. Then our Party Secretary, he says – Nah, we need somethin' partyiotic – and he told us to get ready with Gombrowicz. But the priest, he's the worst. He called all our lasses to himsel' and he says to them: you have to adopt Mary-yoke, for stage-like, you know, and produce him. And what can you do with them multicultures and perversities?

PEASANT B: Aye . . . We've even worse. Some artists came down from Kraków to decorate the club and you know what they did? Past-impressionism! When our village head saw that, how he cussed! So – he says – you think that if it's communal – he says – you can do how you please? *That* you can do when you're an individual! Here on the communal, I see it more abstract-like, he says. And – he says – more rythemic, mioosical . . .

PEASANT A: Pollock's. Aye. But for me mioosic begins with dodecaphonists. What I like best is that synthetic . . .

PEASANT B: Eh, you're but a snob, I tell you. On the outside you go halleluiah aboot them atonal composters but come past yer windows it's nothin' but Bach and Bach, all year round . . .

PEASANT A: Ah, that'll be our gran. She has her years, you know, different generation gap . . .

PEASANT B: Years, aye. You said she was deaf . . .

PEASANT A: Eh, I'm not talking to you. You dedayist . . .

PEASANT B: As if you knew aboot dedayists . . .

Dragon

I still had the rest of the afternoon and almost the entire evening of waiting for my bus. Ready to go, briefcase in hand and coat over my shoulder, I sat in the deep grass on a slope by the roadside. The material for an article on the difficulties and problems of manufacturing traditional harnesses in the village of G was researched thoroughly and so going through my notes again seemed a pointless exercise. I had six hours to kill.

Luckily, the weather was warm and sunny. I stretched out comfortably in the grass. I could see practically the whole village from here. It was big, spreading widely over the surrounding hills and valleys. In the market square, amid the ordinary thatched huts stood two one-storey houses built of stone and the brick building of the new bakery. Below stretched the fields through which ran a lively stream. All this was surrounded by mountains, their tops covered by spruce forest. G was a typical mountain village populated by shepherds and harness-makers. Because of its geographical position it was cut off from major regional centres, yet its inhabitants were relatively cultured folk, keen on education; as I was informed, even a certain recently deceased professor of the oldest university in the country was a native of G.

And so, lying on my stomach in the tall grass, I abandoned myself to the contemplation of nature and the village architecture. Lazily smoking cigarettes and squinting against the sun proved also a reasonable source of amusement. Suddenly I noticed a skinny, shrivelled old man who was squatting nearby. After a while the old man moved towards me holding in his fingers a short, blackened cigarette-end and asked for a light. I offered him my own cigarettes. At first he declined politely and then helped himself to two. He lit up and settled comfortably next to me. I accepted his presence

42

with resignation; after all, he seemed no more boring than the clouds or the mountains.

We started to chat. The old boy turned out to be a retired schoolteacher. He complained about his aching joints and I found this topic amusing enough. He did not take advantage of my position as a journalist by asking favours or trying to sell me village secrets. I was grateful for this and listened to his complaints. We were already smoking a second cigarette when I noticed a group of people gathering in the market square. As far as I could tell from this distance they looked as if they were leaving the church after a high mass, all dressed in their Sunday best. The old man looked in their direction and stated indifferently:

'Oho, they are getting ready . . .'

'For what?'

'You don't know?' He was surprised. 'The twentieth of May . . . Dragon's Day.'

'What dragon?'

'You haven't heard of the dragon of G? People haven't told you?'

'No . . . Or maybe?'

I remembered that, indeed, when I'd said in the club that I was going to G one of my colleagues mentioned a dragon. At that point, however, the waiter brought the vodka and the conversation moved onto a different track. And today, during the interview with the chairman of the village council, the word 'dragon' was also mentioned, perhaps even the 'Dragon's Day'. But, as he hadn't volunteered any more information, I asked my companion to tell me about it.

'Ah, it's an old custom,' he said, 'going back maybe even to pagan times. What happens is that once a year, on the evening of the twentieth day of May, the bonniest lad and the bonniest lass, not more than eighteen, but no less than sixteen, are thrown to the dragon which lives in the cave by the river. Of course the word "bonniest" shouldn't be taken literally –

any healthy boy and girl of the prescribed age are chosen by means of casting lots.'

'And what do we call a dragon?' I asked, amused.

'The dragon is real all right. It's a huge old lizard of unspecified kind. It lives there . . .' The old man pointed his finger towards the alder thicket on the other side of the river. 'Anyway, would you like to see the ceremony? We can join the procession. It'll be passing this way. You will be able to see the whole thing, including the devouring.'

I could not tell whether the old man was making fun of me or simply drivelling. He noticed this and smiled:

'Are you surprised? All our visitors are when they find out about it. But then they get used to it. It's now thirty years since the Society for Public Education organised the first campaign against the dragon, and lost. The problem was also taken up by the government and Party officials but so far they haven't taken any positive steps. You see, the authorities have to reckon with our highlanders' conservatism and love of tradition, and in truth they turn a blind eye to the dragon. Thirty years ago I myself, as an activist of the SPE, spoke out sharply against the dragon and other superstitions rampant in our rural community. I even wrote an article dealing specifically with the dragon. It was called "The Monster Sucks Out Our Vital Juices", and it appeared in our official organ, *The Torch*, which, alas, died a death a good five years before the war.'

'What?' I shouted, quite upset. 'So every year you sentence to death two innocent people, almost children?'

'Well, yes . . . The village doesn't lose much, for the women here are broad of the hip and give birth easily, almost without pain. There's even a saying: "Our lasses very healthy always have an easy birthing." The vicar grumbles about it, he says it goes against the words in the Holy Bible.'

'And what does the dragon do for the rest of the year?'

'He just lies in his cave, digesting, doesn't ask for anything more.'

44

'And if . . . if he were denied the sacrifice? What would happen then?'

'Oh, I don't know. Nobody's tried that yet.'

'And if the monster were killed?'

'It's not that simple. It seems to me that such a rare creature must be under some kind of protection. And he's not as dangerous as you might think . . .You'll see.'

Meanwhile, the procession was moving down the road. It was led by the chairman of the village council, accompanied by two men whom I recognised as the secretary of the local Party cell and the well-known 'people's artist', the local wood-carver Lelek. A few metres behind them two elderly women, wearing starched skirts and beads, led a boy who, despite being no more than eighteen, was tall and broad-shouldered like a fully grown man. His brow was furrowed by a deep horizontal frown. He walked with a rope hanging around his neck but apart from that there were no other signs of force, except maybe for the two women who held him lightly under his arms. The boy's face was covered in sweat and his jaw trembled. Further on two old men in black suits were leading a girl. She was dressed in a silk dress and high-heeled shoes, and sobbed all the way. Time after time she reached into her white handbag for a handkerchief, loudly blowing her nose, putting the handkerchief back into the handbag and taking it out again. Behind them, like a river, flowed the crowd of peasants – men, women and children.

The old man and I stepped off the grass onto the road and joined the procession. The crowd parted and gave us a place at the head, just behind the girl. The procession waded on through the dust of the hot dry road; people sighed and wiped sweat off their brows. After a half-hour march we reached a small footbridge on the river. Here the girl became hysterical. She threw herself on the ground, wailing spasmodically and grabbing people's feet. The crowd stopped to allow the attack to pass. Some lit cigarettes. After a while the girl got up, brushed the dust off her dress and obediently crossed the river. The footbridge was so narrow that it could be crossed only in single file, so the crossing took a long time. Many took their boots off and forded the river.

The place where the procession stopped did not look any different from the remaining stretch of riverbank. Perhaps only the osier and alder thickets were somewhat thicker here. The crowd formed itself into a crescent. The chairman raised his hand and recited:

> *O green dragon, fed with sulphur*
> *we've come to your lair*
> *come outta there, come outta there*
> *take the sacrifice.*

The osier bed rustled and the dragon emerged. It was a reptile about four metres long, an old, blind, mouldy beast. It could hardly stand on its weak, mushy legs.

> *Hear dragon, ye fiery beast,*
> *put ye tail to the west*
> *and ye snout to the east*

recited the chairman again, and seeing the dragon stumbling clumsily he struck it with a stick across the back: 'Shift yerself!' he called out sharply.

The dragon snorted and positioned himself properly as told. The boy, until now quiet and composed, went green and shuffled uneasily.

'Mother,' he mumbled to one of the women holding him, 'I'm gonna be sick.'

The women took him a few steps to one side and held his head with tender care. The boy vomited and wiped his mouth quickly. The women then led him to the dragon and retreated. The boy knelt down, crossed himself and, trying to sound like the chairman, mumbled out:

46

Fare ye well mother dear
and ye golden sun
farewell all ye here
for I am done.

'Amen,' answered the crowd.

The dragon came closer, sniffed the boy, swept him under its belly and tore him apart. He swallowed him in three long gulps. Now it was the girl's turn. She was not crying any more. She kneeled down, wiped her nose and recited the formula. The dragon dealt with her in two snaps of his teeth.

The chairman said:

Hear, ye dragon,
ye took what we gave,
now go back to yer cave.

The dragon stood up with great effort and disappeared into the bushes. The chairman intoned a song. People sang lazily, in fact no one even bothered to sing the last words. The crowd began to disperse. It was time for me, too. My bus was leaving in twenty minutes.

Prophet

I'd been waiting years
Until the Prophet came
He held forth all night
Smoked all my cigarettes
I didn't understand a thing
Stuck in my chair
My right chair leg ached
I couldn't feel my arm
The left chair leg gone numb
I counted all his buttons
And all the stripes on his sweater
He left at dawn

Now I'm waiting again

My Day

In the morning I run to the courts
I offer my services first
To the big-bellied and their fancy females
I smooth down my suit, play a charming fool
Would sir need a perjurer?
Then move on to landlords
The deviant fauna of the middle class
These I nudge casually like a waiter
And into their ear
Need a perjurer?
They snub me in horror
Show their beastly nature
Finally the peasants
Yokels boors clodhoppers
Who arrive on trains in herds
To squabble over their fences
I pull them by their coats and shout
Hey grandad won't you need a perjurer?
When they let me down too
I take myself to the guard-room
And play buttons with the policeman
Tomorrow will be a better day
I say to myself
Bah
The sun will shine

Love

Careful so we don't have a baby
Careful so we don't have a baby

This non-existent baby
Is the apple of our love's eye
We kit it out in the chemist's
Or little shops selling tobacco
And postcards with views of lakes and mountains
And generally take care of it better than if it did exist
And yet
Aaaa
It's crying and wailing
We have to tell it a story then
About precise pincers
Whose touch doesn't hurt at all
And doesn't leave a mark
And then it calms down
Not for long

Function of Poetry

Poetry can't be divorced from life
Poetry is to serve life

A housewife should

Wipe	the dust
Take	rubbish out
Sweep	under the bed
Shake	the rug
Feed	the baby
Go	shopping
Water	plants
Stoke	the fire
Cook	dinner
Wash	dishes
Rinse	glasses
Change	nappies
Mend	trousers
Sew	buttons
Darn	socks
Keep	receipts

and also
do
onethousandandoneother-
thingsofwhichwehaven'tgota-
clue

then read the great Romantics
and nighty-night

Women's War

In the little town called Liplass, inhabited by the people of Older High Luzan culture, once a year the men go away to a nearby oak grove where they drink beer, play chess, billiards and cards (but only for small stakes – the Liplassians are a thrifty folk) or fish in the mill pond. Back in town a war breaks out. Over the year it's all piled up high – the ultimatums, warnings and threats:

'I'm young.'

'I'm older.'

'I have the right.'

'I have more right.'

'My sister-in-law is a cow.'

'Daughter-in-law is terrorising me.'

'Mother-in-law terrorises me.'

'My pot.'

'My frying pan.'

'My comb.'

'Your eyes.'

'My husband.'

'Your lover.'

The fighting goes on throughout the day on the barricades of sideboards and grandfather clocks. First come out the skirmishers: the most and the least pretty women in town. Taking up the most exposed positions, they swear like troopers and trade insults by showing off their bottoms, breasts and legs. And when the stone thrown by the accurate hand of that old hag Zalasova hits the round firm rear of Miss Haase – the carnage begins. The weapons are the usual kitchen utensils, as well as teeth and fingernails. Especially fingernails, for the men, before leaving town, lock up the arsenal and even Roman the policeman (the only man left in town to look after law and order) is armed with a wooden gun. He sits in the police station behind the desk pushed up against the door and tries to make a telephone call to the district headquarters:

'Hallo-hallo . . . hallo-hallo . . .' he says from time to time into the silent receiver.

Before leaving town at dawn, the chief of police sort of accidentally cuts the cable connecting Liplass with the district HQ. There are many wounded; fatalities happen too.

Only children can feel safe, even though they can be seen in the thick of the hottest battle. When occasionally one of the furious harpies knocks down a mother with a baby she immediately picks it up and runs home to change its nappy. A woman who strikes a child, whosoever child it might be, is torn limb from limb. Such was the fate of the student Iza, a nonchalant, modern girl. Slapped by her, the twenty-one-year-old Janek hadn't even wiped off his tears when the young scholar's body lost its form and unity.

In the evening a great sobbing breaks out and the fighting stops. The women smooth out their hair, help each other pull the sideboards back inside their houses and start preparing suppers for their husbands.

But usually the husbands don't eat it. Intoxicated by a long, easy day fragrant with beer, wind and cigars – they fall asleep fast and hard.

Thirteen-year-old

The backyard's parched as ass's skin
Stretched over an empty drum
In open windows dirty linen
Sours in the May sun

A thirteen-year-old with thin
Voice and wrist like a twig
Gives a well-practised swing
To a six-month-old kid

The child under the poisoned sun
Writhes in a pointless torture
When she wraps it in a wet rag
Skinny breastless and swarthy

The fifteen-year-old in the window
Sends her a glance which means
Here comes the new inferno
Of births and miscarriages

Saint Joseph

Of all Catholic saints
I like Saint Joseph best
for he is not a masochist
or some other pervert
he is a craftsman
always with that axe
without an axe
his arm would feel withered
and though his heart was heavy
he raised the Child
whom he knew
was not his son
but God's
or someone else's
and when they were running away from the police
through the night
through the stage set of the inhuman architecture of
    the Rameses
(which is probably why they call policemen pharaohs)
he carried the Child
and the heaviest basket

from Children's Fun and Games

When you are totally bored
get yourself a little angel and a little old man
you play like this:
trip the old man till he smashes his gob on the kerb
the angel drops his head
give the old man five pence
the angel raises his head
break the old man's glasses with a stone
the angel drops his head
give up your seat for the old man
the angel raises his head
empty your pisspot on the old man's head
angel drops his head
tell the old man 'God bless'
the angel raises his head
and so on
then go to bed
in your dream you will see
either a little angel or a little devil
if an angel you win
if the devil you lose
if you see nothing
a draw

Jazz Song

Why have I been taken from my Africa?
I ask you: Why have I been taken from my Africa?
Where are my animals carved in bark
My amulets my blades made of bones of animals . . .
What was the point of me working so
On cotton fields that muffle words
When all that's true is my old song
Of blood sung by the saxophone
What am I doing here?
Been meaning for years
To sail away on a pirate ship
Marking the time on the moon and stars
In cahoots with the bearded skipper
And then gave up scared of the roaring seas
and the skipper turned out to be no globetrotter
Now sunk in Louise's arms I dream
my dreams fading like footprints on water

*

I know those little streets
The creaking sheds on stilts
These are the stamping grounds
Of my childhood dreams

I know those little streets
I walked them through and through
These are the stamping grounds
Of my hungry youth

Killing Auntie

To all who once stood terrified
before the dead perspective of their youth

1

I left home in the afternoon, at four. After a few steps I stopped. I needed a purpose. Nothing came to mind. I resumed my walk like a condemned man, resigned to aimless wandering around the town. I went out for these long and exhausting walks almost every day. But always made sure I had a purpose. Chores, visits. Never did any of that of course. After all, I had nothing to do, no one to visit. But the purpose was there, even though I knew it was a sham.

Today for the first time I realised I had no purpose. I went out without a reason. Those purposeless, lonely walks were murderous. I knew that. In summer, when I walked through woods, fields or overgrown riverbanks, they had at least some justification. They didn't tire me so much. Absorbed into the landscape, becoming part of it, I didn't have to think. I could rest. But in winter the town brought no calm. I ambled around, stopping in front of old gateways and shop windows full of displays wrapped in cellophane but found no solace in either. I appreciated – and understood – the charms of architecture and of the city lights yet saw no point in contemplating them. I longed for a purpose like a sick man longing for a cure. Held hostage by my own nature, I suffered terribly.

I walked slowly and with difficulty. The downy snow, which had fallen during the day, lay on the pavements like heaps of manna. I waded through them. The interminable circling of the streets was wearing me out. I knew that overcome by exhaustion I would soon reach a point when I would think of returning home with pleasure and, barely standing, rejoice at the sight of my window. But it was no consolation. I knew too that back at home, resting on my bed, I would reach for the mirror and look at myself. For a long time.

I examined my face several times a day, every day, looking for signs of maturity or old age. But the face remained stubbornly young. Nine years of youth lay before me like an endless fallow field unfit for farming. On top of that all my limbs were in perfect order and I was in rude health. There was no salvation. Aimless wandering in bad weather was no fun. Return home was impossible. The thought that I could spend the rest of the afternoon and the evening poring over recommended reading set at the university barred my way. There was only the street, which ruled out any surprises.

In my wandering I could never keep away from the centre. All the excuses could be found within the surrounding boulevards. Today I hadn't dared to break my habit. Yet the main streets and squares tired me with their noise and crowds. I turned surreptitiously into a narrow, almost empty street close to the main thoroughfare. I found myself in the middle of a labyrinth of old streets bordering on the centre yet completely isolated from it. By the gates hung bells on wires. On the backs of crabs, unicorns and little bears carved over the pediments lay snow. The labyrinth wasn't big. I could cross it both ways in ten minutes. So I walked as slowly as I could, trying to keep my strides short, resisting the temptation to stop. I reached the stone wall of the Capuchin monastery. I knew that in a few seconds I'd come to a small square by the river. From there I could see the tarmac alley which I'd have to take as my return route. The prospect made me want to stop several times and run the other way. But the route led through the streets I knew by heart; there was no point in running away from the tarmac alley straight back into the embrace of a noisy road.

When I got to the end of the wall I stopped for a moment's rest, like a swimmer about to plunge back into the water. I looked to one side. Two stone angels wearing snowy hats stood guarding the small gate in front of a church. The courtyard

before the little church was an oasis of peace. Over the surrounding wall, below street level, tree branches stuck out from
the orchard on the other side. They were covered in snow. I
was long hardened to all kinds of soppiness and so was able to
look calmly at the relief on the walls and trees growing in the
cloister, which I had known so well since childhood.

From the door leading into the enclosure a bearded monk
came out with a broad wooden shovel and began to clear the
snow. He didn't pay any attention to me but I felt awkward.
I stepped out of his way and began to study the relief on the
wall. The monk kept shovelling the snow, panting laboriously.
The longer we were alone the more awkward I felt. In the end
I reached the point of no return. Slowly, I approached the
gate and entered the church. I took a quiet pew at the back. I
was not alone. Three elderly women knelt in front of me, two
in the pew, one on the stone floor. Above the altar flickered a
little flame like a small red heart. Next to the side altar shone a
luminous entrance to a small cavern. Inside it, behind a strong
grille, lay the golden arm of a seventeenth-century hero.

Once I knew well a legend about the hero who bequeathed
his golden arm, a gift from the king, to the Capuchin order.
Today some details were missing from memory. Hiding in
the pew I took for myself the role of an observer. A banal
and thankless role: there was nothing to observe here. From
the sacristy a surpliced monk came out with a stole over his
neck. Briskly he crossed the floor and shut himself in the
confessional. I didn't see his face well but with his beard and
a high brow he seemed to me beautiful. He was tall, broad-
shouldered, not young. The trellis on the confessional door
closed, the stole was hung outside. I thought that at this time
it was unlikely anyone would come to confession. By the altar
I spotted the same monk who had been sweeping the snow.
He was performing some strange ritual which involved a lot of
kneeling. It was high time for me to leave; I just didn't feel like
it. In the empty church (the three women being gone), facing

the mute expectation of the priest-confessor, I felt I had found my role. I got up and walked up to the confessional, knelt and knocked. For a fleeting moment I felt fear and stage fright, but I didn't back down. Something rustled inside the confessional and the priest welcomed me with a Latin formula. I took a deep breath and recited back:

'I last came to confession more or less six – no – seven years ago.'

'Why so long, son?'

'I lost faith.'

'What else, my son?'

The priest's voice was weary and passionless. My blasphemous confession didn't make much impression on him. I was crestfallen. I hesitated. I didn't know what to say. Desperately I was trying to remember the formulae from school confessions.

'Since then . . . since then I offended the Lord with many sins . . .'

'Confess them, my son.'

'I was . . .' I hesitated again. 'I was disobedient with my superiors . . . I lied, and then bore false witness against my brother . . .'

I was getting hopelessly confused.

'What else, my son?'

I frowned and after some thought whispered triumphantly:

'I sinned against the sixth commandment.'

The priest stirred in his seat.

'Many times?'

'Oh no, not that many,' I sighed regretfully.

'What else, my son?'

I couldn't sense in my confessor's voice any concern. Feverishly I was looking for words with which I could reveal to him the full horror of my inner life, which should terrify a holy man. In vain. The priest was already whispering the final formula. In a moment I would hear him knock on the confessional and walk away defeated. I quickly pressed my lips to the wooden lattice and whispered earnestly:

'Father, holy Father,' I corrected myself, 'I concealed one sin.'

The priest leaned to the lattice. I lowered my voice.

'I concealed a terrible sin . . .' I went for a dramatic pause and then whispered emphatically:

'I killed a human being.'

Ah, no more indifferent 'what else, my son?' now. The priest was panting. After a moment's silence he asked in an unnaturally loud voice:

'Whom?'

'My aunt.'

'Oh, my son . . . It's a terrible sin, terrible.'

The priest was lost for words. Now I was cold and to the point.

'How did it happen?'

In the priest's voice, apart from a hellish, almost unchristian curiosity, I detected a note of enthusiasm.

'Holy Father,' I whispered gravely, ''tis unfitting to speak about.'

'In confession one has to tell everything, everything,' he insisted pleadingly.

I decided to be succinct.

'OK then. I killed her with a hammer.'

'Hammer . . . Oh my son, it's a terrible sin, a grave sin . . .'

'Holy Father, more important than the gate of Hades is my soul,' I replied courteously.

The priest fell silent for a while and then asked:

'Had your aunt wronged you in any way?'

'No.'

'So why did you kill her?'

I hung my head.

'Were you led to it by the repulsive jingle of gold?'

The priest was trying to rise to his role. I felt grateful.

'No, Father, to the contrary.'

'Why to the contrary?'

'Killing my aunt I deprived myself of my main means of support. She gave me board and lodging.'

'So why did you do it?'

'I'm a murderer, Father.'

The priest fell silent again. And after a while:

'How old are you, my son?'

'Twenty-one.'

'Oh, twenty-one . . . Was it . . . was it your first time?'

'First what, Father?'

'Had you killed before?'

'No, Father. I would have confessed, wouldn't I?'

'True. Oh my son, repent your deed and cry over your soul.'

'I can't repent, Father.'

'Why, my son?'

'I'm a hardened sinner.'

'Oh my son,' the priest was hopelessly confused. 'Oh my son, cry over your soul . . .'

But then the curiosity won the upper hand.

'But you had to have a motive. Why did you kill?'

'I don't know, Father.'

He hesitated.

'You are not . . . sick, are you?'

'No, Father.'

'So why, my son? Why?'

'I sought peace in crime.'

'You can find peace only in prayer.'

'I'm too young to waste my days on prayers.'

'But, son,' the priest got irritated. 'There are so many other sins . . .' He stopped abruptly. After a while he started again: 'Are you feeling weak and abandoned?'

'Oh I do, Father.'

'Then repent your sin and cry with me. Difficult years of

prison, provided you spend them in remorse and penitence, will atone for your crime.'

'I've no intention of going to prison.'

'How have you managed to hide your crime?'

'I haven't. I've done it only this morning.'

'What have you done with the corpse?'

'For now it's in my kitchen. I'll try to get rid of it.'

'How . . .' He bit his tongue, apparently realising the question was not quite in keeping with his work as a confessor.

'I've got a plan.'

'I don't want to know. Do you repent of your sin, my son?'

'I can't, Father.'

'Repent, my son.' He was pleading with me tearfully. 'Or you'll go to hell.'

'Is it horrible, Father?'

'Oh, son!' cried out the priest, grateful for my question.

And he began to paint the picture. The way he was doing it told me he was a just a catechist. But his picture of hell surpassed all the best lessons I could remember from childhood. My confessor was inspired. Throughout his life he had been unleashing the horrors of hell to scare small-time sinners for their pranks played on teachers, their masturbation or laziness, only to have his efforts rewarded with today's confession. The grand vision of inferno painted for the benefit of such an extraordinary criminal was the sweet fruit that fell into his lap in an empty church, out of the blue, on an afternoon one could expect nothing from. Necessity breeds inventors, necessity breeds heroes. Today I learned that necessity – or rather need – breeds artists. I had seen many reproductions of Old Masters depicting hell but none had come close to my confessor's tirade. That was real hell. Seething, blazing, putrid. I easily forgave my confessor some catechetic naivety for the sweeping power of his vision.

The church was empty again. The monk had put out all the lights except for the little red lamp. There were only the two of us, the hero's golden arm, and hell. At last the priest ran out of breath.

'My son,' he pleaded, 'repent your crime.'

'I can't, father.'

'Then I can't give you absolution.'

It all began to turn nasty.

'Then I'll walk away with hell in my heart.'

I got up to my feet, as if ready to leave. The priest rustled hurriedly inside the confessional.

'No, son, don't go away.' He lowered his voice and I heard in his words a playful note.

'If you can find in you perfect remorse, the most pleasing to the Lord, an imperfect one will be enough . . . Think of all the horrors of hell and fear the deed which condemns you to such torture. That will be enough.'

The priest's voice was so sympathetic I was ready to express my imperfect remorse. Still, I held back. Showing an imperfect remorse would give my confessor a paltry satisfaction. This extraordinary confession would have a very cheap and trivial epilogue in a common criminal's fear of chains and fire. So I said:

'Father, an imperfect remorse will not atone for such a crime before the Lord.'

The priest was delighted.

'My son,' he said, 'words like these suffice for a remorse.'

'It's not worth much, though.'

'Son, I'm crying for your soul,' whispered the priest, 'I truly am.'

He felt his inspiration was waning but still could not let go of me. The confession got stuck in a dead end. I pitied the priest. Anxiously, I started looking for a way out of the impasse. In the end I suggested:

'My crime is still fresh today. I'm still breathing blood. But tomorrow, or in a few days' time, if God lets me live that long, perhaps the grace of remorse will come to me.'

66

'Come tomorrow then, my son,' hurriedly advised the priest. 'In the afternoon, or in the evening. Between four and six. I'll be waiting every day.'

The priest sounded excited and joyous. He appreciated the chance I gave him. Today's confession will be more than just a beautiful moment in his life. It will open a difficult, glorious path to the salvation of a murderer, a path full of terrible mysteries. I have elevated my cleric to the level of a missionary converting cannibals, of a Saint Hieronymus taming a lion. He was pleased like child, and it pleased me too. When I rose from my knees, the priest reminded me once more:

'So, between four and six, four and six p.m.'

His voice trembled with the anxiety of a parting lover.

2

Every time I opened my eyes in the morning Auntie was already on her feet. Humming in her low alto voice she bustled around the stove, preparing our breakfast. The simpleness and good nature of this woman were too much of an everyday occurrence to make any impression on me. Nevertheless, from time to time, there were moments they moved me, though recently they more often irritated me. Auntie earned her living as a sort of middleman in the local wool trade or some such business; I was never really interested in that. She was working her butt off.

Apart from myself, a twenty-one-year-old shaver, Auntie provided also for her old mother and her crippled sister. Both lived in a remote small town in the mountains. They visited us more than four times a year. I hated those visits. When Granny, wrapped up in black frocks, her ears smeared around with some white pasty medicine, sat at the table, it was really revolting. I felt even more disgust for her daughter – a young apathetic hunchback with bottle-bottom spectacles. They were both very devout and crossed themselves eagerly before every dish. Auntie, once a beautiful and worldly woman, with them suddenly remembered which church she belonged to. The dinners were better then, and that was the only plus to those visits.

Auntie maintained she would like to have the old mother and the cripple sister with her but it was impossible because our flat was just too small. And she had to keep her eye on me while I was studying. This was not true. I have no doubt she preferred to share the flat with her favourite nephew than with her half-dead mother and a blockhead sister. I was the only person Auntie truly loved. She liked it when I whistled during my morning shave in the bathroom, or polished off with gusto her scrambled eggs. She knew I had to finish my studies and she spared no effort to make sure I did. However, there was a limit to how much effort she could spare, and that limit was not far off.

Auntie had reached the point when she needed a quiet recuperation before the terminal advance of old age. And yet she still worked like a horse. She carried big packs of merchandise, went on business trips, often sleeping on the train. She did pay for it with her heart, her liver, varicose veins. She was trying to cure them, seeing the doctors and following their orders. But often life made these impractical. So Auntie suffered on, now and again letting out a groan or a sigh, and who knows – perhaps that was the cause of the whole affair. Normally she bore her illnesses and old age with gallant heroism. She took care of herself, was not above a discreet touch of make-up, and generally kept her spirits up, almost every morning waking me up with a joke. Truly, when I look back at those times, I have to admit she was indeed a very, very good woman.

Certainly, the cause of this whole situation could not lay in the small misunderstandings which naturally took place between us. In fact, if I remember correctly, no such incidents occurred that day. It was March, the frost still held fast. Auntie had to breathe on the window pane to check the temperature on the outside thermometer. It was about ten o'clock. The snow glistened on the metal windowsill. But inside the room it was actually warm. I remember that when I was putting my slippers on, Auntie made some chirpy remark, which irritated me. Without hurrying things, I put on my trousers, shirt and a jumper. I ate my breakfast of scrambled eggs, bread and coffee with appetite. Auntie asked me what time my lectures began, to which I replied that at ten and that therefore I had plenty of time. After breakfast Auntie asked me to hammer a nail into the wall so that she could hang a mirror. This new task gave me a certain satisfaction. The hammer especially proved to be an oddly pleasant tool to handle, something I had not paid any attention to before. When the nail was hammered in and I sat sprawling lazily on the stool, I was still holding the hammer in my hands. I was playing with it.

Auntie was getting ready to go out. She looked into the room, opened and closed the sideboard, checked the gas and bent down to pull on her boots. Then I walked up to her from behind and with all my strength whacked her twice on the side of her head.

There was no doubt Auntie was a corpse. She lay still, a small trickle of blood pouring out of god knows where as there was no visible wound. I grabbed her by the shoulders and turned her face up. There was no doubt – she was a corpse.

'Corpse,' I pronounced half loud. 'Corpse, corpse, corpse . . .' I sort of sang to myself, and felt uneasy.

Auntie's eyes were opened wide, her moist teeth peered from behind parted lips. And the blood – from her nose, mouth, ears – tiny rivulets flowing into puddles on the floor. This fleshy, ripened body ceased to be fifty-four years old, ceased to feel pain, suffer illnesses, to enjoy itself. Shapely though overworked hands were now wood. This body was so alien I found it impossible to feel at that moment any pity or regret.

I became a little nauseous. I went back to my room and lay on the bed. I felt my hand sticking to the sheets. It turned out that both hands had blood on them, god knows how it happened as there wasn't really that much blood, and I wasn't touching it. So I went to the bathroom. It angered me to see I was leaving bloody marks on the tap. It struck me as too literary. Washing my hands, all the time I felt in my stomach and in my throat this morning's breakfast: sweet coffee and peppery scrambled eggs. And before me – Auntie's corpse. I bent over the toilet bowl, pushed two fingers down my throat and vomited. After I threw it all up, once more I thoroughly washed my hands, rinsed my mouth and drank some water. Then carefully examined my face in the mirror.

I looked bad, but that could be put down to vomiting. At any rate, I saw in myself nothing of a murderer. I still had the same lock of hair on my forehead, same lips, nose and the grey good-natured eyes of a luckless boy who at twenty-one was still just an awkward teenager. I took out a cigarette and, smoking, walked to the kitchen, where I sat over Auntie's corpse. As I smoked the fear began to rise. It was making me sweat. I was cold and nauseated. My fingers, by now burnt by the cigarette, seemed so weak and helpless I could hardly believe what they had been capable of.

And yet they were capable. I felt pride, which alas was immediately soured by icy, slimy fear. It seemed there was nothing left for me but to go down and report at the police station, or simply stop in the street the first militiaman and bring him here. The militiaman: red face of the people, matter-of-fact, unbelieving tone – I was gripped by spasm of terror. I dragged myself back to bed and tried to calm down. I was talking to myself in a half-voice, as any soundless sentence would have been drowned out by the pounding fear.

'Calm down, my boy, calm down. Everything will be all right. We'll manage . . . Ha ha, we will . . .' Something broke loose inside me. 'Never mind, it's nothing. I know it sounds paradoxical. Never mind, it's nothing. You'll live . . . We'll get out of it . . . Remember' – I raised my finger – 'you are twenty-one years old. You must live. Your whole life is before you. Women, travel, work, adventures. You are twenty-one years old. Twenty-one. You are young, young . . .'

I was telling myself this and believed it all, though I did not feel at all twenty-one years old, let alone that it was a good reason I should live, and pleasantly at that. This does not mean I felt physically weak. I could have got up and lifted off the floor that heavy chair with my left hand. But why? What for? Don't move, calm down.

I looked at my watch. It was ten. I still could make it to the lecture. The thought of getting out of the flat filled me with energy. I put my boots on, but as soon as I laced them up I changed my mind. This special day called for some little celebration. Devil knows why I thought that by turning up at the lecture I might be tempting fate. I unlaced my old skiing boots, took them off and put on my slippers again. I carried out these small tasks with precision and diligence. I was terrified but my movements were calm now. I began to consider the ways of disposing of the corpse. It seemed child's play. I'll chop the body up, flush some parts down the loo, burn some, take others away in parcels and throw them in the river or bury them. Bury where? Ah, it's a trifle. I know a quiet place in the wood on the outskirts of town.

I felt light-headed and carefree. I decided to carry out the plan without further ado. I went into the kitchen with an open penknife. I started with a finger. It turned out to be not that simple. The blade was blunt, the flesh gave in with difficulty, chafing and tearing. The bone just would not cut. I put away the penknife and fetched an axe. I swung it and the finger sprang off. At the same time I was struck in the eye by the tip of the thumb. I picked up the finger and dropped it down the toilet bowl. It floated in the yellowish water like a pale sausage. I flushed the loo. The water gushed, snatched the finger and sucked it into the black void, but after a while the finger floated back to the surface. I yanked the chain. The pipes rumbled deeply, the water rose and filled the bowl. The finger disappeared. I took a piss. The finger resurfaced. The water subsided slowly. I fished out the wet finger and held it hopelessly between my own two fingers.

Apparently, that was not the way. It became clear to me that disposing of this hefty, sixty-eight-kilo body, depriving it of its full, overripe figure with its bale of fresh skin, was not going to be as easy as it seemed to me, fed on the literature from the 'time of contempt'. The corpse defended its individuality, its natural right to biological decay. Somewhat embarrassed, I returned to the kitchen and laid the hacked-off finger on Auntie's breast.

There was something of a gesture of reconciliation in that.

3

Around midday I went out. The street was freezing cold, hostile. The sun, which in the morning had lit so beautifully the snow on the windowsill, had disappeared. It was grey and cold. I felt hungry. Up till now Auntie cooked lunch at home. If she was away I ate at any old place. I stepped into a third-class bar on the corner. It was full. There was one free table in the middle of the room but I retreated. Sweaty, yellow-brown lacquered walls, stuffy stench of the room, trivial faces of the eaters – all that disgusted me. I walked on. I was approaching the town centre when it came to my mind that a day like this could be honoured with a good meal at a first-class restaurant.

In the window an enormous salmon in red caviar lay in a wreath of parsley. From behind the matted glass peered lush leaves of exotic plants, creating the impression of a perfect refuge from the freezing street. I pushed the door open and headed for the cloakroom. The cloakroom lady was very tall and very big. Much bigger than Auntie. I assessed her at some eighty kilos and thanked god it was not her corpse I had in my flat. I was about to unbutton my coat when I saw the waiter standing at the entrance to the room. The waiter was a black-haired man of about thirty-five. Dressed in routine waiters' garb: black, slightly wide trousers, white apron, white shirt. He was playing with a napkin, looking in my direction. I felt I was afraid of waiters. At that moment I thought of one thing only: avoid a situation where he could come near me and say something. I walked back to the cloakroom lady.

'Can I make a phone call?'

Straight away I realised what a stupid idea that was; I could have asked for a packet of cigarettes, even those expensive ones, foreign, which could not be got anywhere else. But it was too late. I picked up the receiver and under the cloakroom lady's unfriendly gaze I dialled a fictitious number, which nevertheless began with a 5, like all other telephone numbers in our town. I heard a woman's voice.

'Hello,' I said calmly. 'May I speak to Andrzej, please?'

When told 'Wrong number,' I apologised and thanked the woman sincerely.

Back on the street I was hit by sharp wind. I thought of my flat and happily turned towards home. Home sweet home. When at last I reached home, still dressed, in my coat and hat, I looked into the kitchen.

Auntie had not changed. Except for the blood around her and on her face, which had dried into a blackish brown scab. I took my coat off and, smoking a cigarette, I began to devise a plan of action. Without question, I had to remove the corpse from the kitchen and make some lunch. The gas was weak. So I decided to light a fire under the kitchen stove and cook myself a proper meal. In the sideboard I found a couple of red cutlets, bread, frankfurters, butter, eggs and potatoes in a basket. There was also tea and even a bottle of Hungarian wine, which Auntie must have hidden there for some special occasion.

I started peeling the potatoes. I was not good at it. Until now I had hardly ever peeled potatoes. Auntie always prepared our meals and I helped only when my manly strength or my manly height was called for. By the second potato I cut my finger. The wound was not big but deep and bled profusely. Clumsily pulling up the shirtsleeve with my other, healthy but dirty hand, I ran to the sink. The tiny wound hit by a stream of cold water began to smart. I put my finger into my mouth and sucked it. The pain abated but every time I took the finger out of my mouth, the pale, barely visible slit began to fill with scarlet blood. I went to the cupboard with the first-aid kit and rummaging through it found some gauze, plaster and iodine. There was no other disinfectant. It took me a long time before I managed to dress my wound and tie on the finger a nice tight knot.

I sat at the kitchen table miserable and worn out, nursing my wounded finger in my fist. Hunger and cigarettes pressed on my brain like a heavy grey substance. I had no strength left to finish peeling the potatoes. I'll have frankfurters with scrambled eggs and bread. Absentmindedly I dragged myself to the sideboard to fetch a saucepan. Suddenly something tripped me up. I struggled to keep my balance and, desperately clutching at anything, I banged my head right against the edge of the sideboard.

'Fuck!' I cursed loudly and madly.

The object which tripped me up was Auntie's corpse. Overwhelming pain paralysed me briefly. Yet, hungry and exhausted, I found in me new layers of strength. I was able to refrain from ignobly taking it out on the inanimate object which had caused me pain. The cause of my frustration should be pacified so that in the future similar accidents could be avoided. I went about it with blunt, angry assiduousness. I wrapped my hands under Auntie's shoulders and lifted her. She was very heavy. As I pulled her along I smelled an unpleasant odour coming out of her open mouth. I turned my face away. Suddenly I felt the body putting up an insurmountable resistance. I pulled with all my strength but it would not budge. It turned out Auntie's foot was hooked around one of the sideboard's legs. I had to lay her down and unhook the damn foot. I tried a different hold. I grabbed her by the wrists and began pulling her across the floor. This was not easy either. The hands were stiff, unwieldy and difficult to steer with. Still, I managed to gain some ground. After a while the head hit the threshold. The first part of the job was behind us. Now I raised the head, then the shoulders, and pulled them over the threshold.

The corridor was narrow and cluttered. The bathroom door was hung in such a way that the body had to be turned around by 180 degrees. That required a well-thought-out plan and precise execution. First thing to do was to remove all possible objects which stood in the way of the body. So I took down the washbowl from the small chest standing by the wall, then the carton with wool, and put them away. Then with some effort I lifted the chest and put that away too. Slowly I was forgetting about my hunger and fatigue. I felt good, like at any noble manual labour, not the perfunctory kind but one requiring a creative element. Bit by bit, carefully, I was pushing the corpse over the threshold, trying to position it so that later I could easily pull it inside the bathroom. Now and again I spoke to myself, giving myself warnings, compliments, reprimands and words of encouragement:

'Well done. Yes . . . No, no, no, we won't get anywhere this way. Wait . . . Wait, my friend. Now. Yes, that's it. See?'

Suddenly the doorbell rang. The sharp short sound cut through the soft shuffle of my work and effortful panting. Crouching by the corpse I froze still. I held my breath. The floorboards at the opposite end of the corridor creaked gently. I remembered that Mazan, a fellow student from my year, was to visit me today. A terrible swot. At the same time it crossed my mind that the room was dark and the kitchen windows faced the courtyard so the light should not betray me. I realised all that very quickly and the intruder soon began to bore me and irritate me. I was not scared at all; he was simply disturbing me. Mazan rang the doorbell again, waited a bit . . . then tried knocking. Then the door rattled and I heard something like muffled rapping and scraping. Mazan was writing me a note. Finally he finished writing and walked away with a loud clank of his skiing boots, which I'd somehow missed when he came. I was very tempted to read his note. After waiting a good while, I quietly opened the door and picked up the note off the floor. 'Jurek, I came to see you at 6. Come to the lectures tomorrow, we'll need you. Ciao. Tadek.'

'Ah, there we are,' I said aloud. 'There we are . . .'

This was just what I expected. And I was not disappointed. I knew too what they would be needing me for. My friends were organising tea with dancing, and wanted me to help. I could not care less, but I could not afford not to get involved.

I returned to my work. Pulling the corpse into the bathroom turned out to be easier than expected. Loading it into the bath was not so easy. The body was falling through my hands, resisting me. Now the head, now the feet knocked about the floor tiles. At long last I managed to fit it in. The legs stuck up in the air and the skirt slipped halfway down the thighs. Automatically I pulled it over the knees, only to realise the pointlessness of the gesture, as sooner or later I would have to strip the corpse naked anyway. I found the prospect rather embarrassing. I had never seen Auntie naked. Only once, in passing, I saw her bare buttocks and then for the rest of the day felt weird in her company.

I returned to the kitchen and on the gas cooker made scrambled eggs, which I covered with cold frankfurters and bread. Luckily by now the gas was better.

4

In the morning I woke up fresh and rested. I jumped out of bed and did a few vaguely gymnastic motions. The room was a bit chilly, I had appetite, good humour and felt really young. Auntie's canary sent off from his cage a peel of brilliant trills:

'Tru – tiu – tu . . .'

I echoed him:

'Tiu – tiu . . . Good morning, little birdie. Good morning, Kraków, good morning, sun . . . Good morning, good morning!'

I ran to fetch a bag with seeds and served the birdie a copious spoonful in his bowl. The wall glittered with playful sunny bunnies. It was cold outside but warmer than yesterday. The thermometer was showing minus six. It was 8.20 a.m. Phew, at last I had had a good night's sleep. I had slept almost ten hours. Now I felt rested, strong, young and independent. Whistling, I ran to the bathroom. I would have loved to have had a bath but unfortunately the bath tub was filled with the corpse.

I stood in front of the mirror.

'Good morning, Jurek,' I smiled. 'Hello, Jerzy.'

I ran the tap and washed myself from waist up.

'Good morning, Auntie.' I turned towards the bath.

'*How did my love*
sleep in the tub?'

I was singing, crying and shaking off the cold water. After drying myself with a thick hairy towel, I started to shave. I was a little bit cold but did not put my shirt on, showing off instead my arms and shoulders, perhaps still rather boyish for my age. While getting dressed I was doing gymnastics all the time, and hummed to myself under my nose.

I put the kettle on the stove and started preparing breakfast. Once more I considered my situation. It was not bad. I was confident, but without the easy optimism which momentarily had swept over me immediately after killing Auntie. I was aware now that disposing of the corpse would require a long effort but I believed I was up to it. Auntie's sudden disappearance should not arouse any suspicions from the neighbours or friends. She often went away without any warning and could be absent even for several days at a time. I decided that after ten days – during which time I should certainly manage to get rid of the corpse – I would start a search. First I would write to Granny, then to friends and Auntie's business associates in other towns, and finally I would place an ad in the press and call the police.

The food in the larder would last me only for two, three days. After breakfast I searched the flat for the money. In Auntie's handbag, in the linen cupboard between the sheets and in the drawer of her night table I found notes totalling one thousand and seven hundred zlotys. That should tide me over for now. Later I might sell Auntie's clothes and her jewellery: her wedding ring, the ruby ring and the small necklace. Apart from that, inside the corpse's mouth I should find a golden bridge, though with selling that I should wait a bit. At any rate, I'm financially secure for a few months. Then there will be summer, I can go away camping, and in the last year at university I'll find a job.

I already started thinking of finding a suitable, not too absorbing employment. But first things first – I had to get cracking with getting rid of the corpse. I knew I could not do it in one go, that the job had to be spread over several days and that I would have to be extremely careful. It crossed my mind that part of the body I could burn in the stove. Frequent trips with parcels containing bits of the corpse struck me as too risky.

The lectures started in the afternoon. So I decided to get on with it now. What I could not decide on was whether to light the kitchen stove or the one in the bedroom. Eventually I settled on both. The flat was pretty cold. Although I sleep and spend most of my time in the bedroom, recently I'd got to like sitting around the kitchen. Perhaps it was that silly power which brings the murderer to the scene of his crime, which one reads so much about in novels. Of course I did not feel a murderer. Killing Auntie was in my case the result of so many interlocking mental states, of depression and complexes, which I had analysed and digested so many times before, that analysing and digesting them all over again would only be another pointless routine. In fact my engagement with the corpse ruled out in advance any element of remorse, if I had any in the first place. The corpse was simply my partner in a hazardous game, in which admittedly I couldn't win anything, but on the other hand could lose my life. I even had a kind of respect for it, the way one usually has for a strong opponent.

I had a bit of a stage fright before lighting the stove. It was a much more difficult task than peeling potatoes. I tried not to admit it to myself, though. With a poker and a coal spade I swept out the ash, revealing the bare grille. Quite a big proportion of the ashes missed the bucket and ended up on the floor. But I did not worry too much about it. The floor needed to be scrubbed anyway. It had small puddles of Auntie's dried-up blood on it, as well as a few drops of mine from the unfortunate finger. I thought I would have to wash the shirt too; its sleeves were stained with blood when I was trying to put dressing on my wound. Taking bloodied linen to a laundry would in my situation be rather risky.

I placed on the grille a few sheets of old newspapers, and on top of them a few dry splinters of wood. Only then I decided to place among all this flammable material some pieces of coal. The first match went out the moment I brought it near the stove. The second and the third likewise. I remembered then that inside the stove there was some kind of draught which puts out small flames. I hit on the idea of lighting a piece of paper outside the stove and putting it inside only when it was properly burning. Alas, I ran out of matches. I looked on the stove; I found several boxes but all empty. A search of the entire flat was equally fruitless. I was delighted when on Auntie's night table I found a box which was heavy and rattled when I picked it up. But all the matches inside were burnt. There was no other way: I had to go downstairs and buy matches. I accepted it without grumbling.

I had to go out to buy cigarettes anyway, of which I had only two left; they would not last me till midday. In the kiosk on the corner I purchased two boxes of matches – one for my pocket, the other for the household – a packet of cigarettes and today's paper.

I could not refuse myself the pleasure of leafing through the pages before lighting the stove. I sat on the stool and checked the headlines. I always started with news reports, although the names of diplomats or international events did not interest me at all. Inside there was an article with quite an attractive title but so long and grey I knew I would never be able to read it. Below I found a column in italics signed by a local hack, from whom I could not expect anything good. Finally I reached the back page, my favourite. Among the gossip, small ads, weather forecasts and other short pieces I found the following title:

'Matricide on the death row'

I read on:

'Yesterday concluded a court case against Edward Wasacz, aged 19, from the village Żylin, in Dąbrowa district, accused of carrying out a killing on the person of his mother Weronika Wąsacz, aged 45. On the 27th of last month the accused returned home in a state of inebriation and when his mother remonstrated with him he hit her on the face with his fist. The woman began to scream and cry for help, in response to which her son struck her on the head with an axe, thus causing an open fracture of the skull. Following this, the murderer buried the victim's body under a pile of manure in the yard. Thanks to energetic investigation the perpetrator was arrested just 48 hours later. The County Court, having proved his guilt, sentenced the pathological killer to death.'

I found no parallel between this piece of news and my current situation. There was absolutely no psychological similarity between me and the peasant from Dąbrowa district. Nevertheless, I read the column carefully several times. I smiled to myself, imagining the sly drunk burying his corpse in a pile of shit. I also calculated how long is 48 hours and whether it had passed since my killing of the Auntie. It turned out it had not.

'Good,' I said aloud and kneeled before the stove, matches in hand.

I lit a sheet of newspaper and threw it inside. It curled up in flames and fell on the coal in a charred, scrunched-up crust. The stove was black and cold again. I lit another sheet and placed it in such a way as to direct the flames onto the dry wood. And then quickly put the burning match to the papers put in the stove earlier. The flame rose clear and high. The wood began to burn. Triumphantly I closed the stove hatch. Through the long slits in the iron hatch flickered playful bright light. Alas, it started to weaken and soon the stove gaped at me with empty sockets. It died. I got annoyed. I stuffed in as much paper as the stove would take and went to the larder where Auntie kept a bottle of kerosene; there was still some left at the bottom. I lit the paper and poured the kerosene on the feeble flame. The inside of the stove burst into light and in a trice everything was in flames. I watched as the wood caught fire and how the flame cuddled up to the coal with little sparks and made it glow.

I loved fire. As a child I could spend hours watching the charming and yet fleeting shapes of burning objects, their last slow throes before annihilation. I liked watching old newspapers and rubbish transmogrify in their last moments into burning craters, assuming blindingly white forms. I liked watching the miraculous transformation of frail dry flakes now crackling in scarlet opulence. A few prods with the poker inside the stove stirred up a golden blizzard. I put in some more pieces of coal and closed the hatch.

It was much nicer in the kitchen now. Of course the freshly kindled fire could not yet give much heat but I knew it would soon be warm. I put a saucepan with water on the range and got busy with lunch. I fortified my tea with the Hungarian wine and checked the stove. Most of the coal was now glowing red. I took some glowing embers on the pan and carried it to the stove in the bedroom. Then I stoked both stoves with more coal. I felt like a lord in my modest castle. I looked into the pantry to compose a menu for lunch. First of all the cutlets, which had been lying on the shelf for two days. I will fry them with potatoes. Fried eggs will make an excellent side dish too. A soup crossed my mind but I dismissed it as too complicated. I put on a big kettle of water. I checked for sugar in the sugar bowl and it turned out there was plenty. I spread the newspaper on the floor, brought in the basket, took out the knife and began peeling potatoes. It was not difficult at all. I worked slowly, unhurriedly, calmly. Just when I finished the third potato I felt a pang of anxiety. I felt vaguely as if I had committed a kind of desertion. It was all too pretty, too pastoral. After all, with all this calm and confidence one must not forget that there is a corpse nearby. And it can cause trouble. One silly accident and the crime will be out. I checked the stove. The heat was wonderful. I pushed the potatoes aside and went over to the bathroom.

When I stood over the corpse I had to reprimand myself again for being absentminded and impulsive. I had brought no tools with me. I returned to the kitchen to fetch the axe. But with the axe I stood over the corpse just as helpless as without it. The corpse was lying on the bottom of the tub, which precluded any sensible chop. I could of course hack at its face, open up the stomach or cut the chest but that would not advance the job in any real way. My eyes alighted on the feet, sticking up above the edge of the bath. Why not start with the legs? I took a good swing and struck, aiming more or less for the middle of the tibia between the foot and the knee, at the point where the leg was resting on the rim of the bath. I struck and the bathroom was filled with a deep metallic boom. The bath rang out like a bell. I'd missed. I'd only scratched the calf, tearing up the stocking and the skin, and made a dent in the bath. The boom seemed interminable. I heard it out patiently, feeling terribly guilty. When the boom died out I tapped myself on the forehead.

'Think, man. Think. Chopping off legs with an axe,' I was explaining to myself, 'has no sense whatsoever. Equally pointless is chopping them off here. Rather, you should aim to obtain smaller pieces, ready to be put in the stove. And lastly – there is no point in chopping legs clad in stockings and shoes.'

So I unlaced the shoes, pulled them off the dead feet and stood them to attention in the room in front of Auntie's bed. Then I pulled up the skirt and unclasped the stockings. I rolled them up into a ball and threw them in the stove. From the larder I fetched a small and rather blunt saw. I positioned myself and had a first go. It was not too bad. I realised that by resting my hand just above the corpse's knee I could saw the leg into pieces any size I liked, just like they do it in the country when sawing birch branches which go straight into the stove. So first, I had to disconnect the foot. I cleared my throat to emphasise the gravity of the work, and began:

Shrrt-Shrrt ... shrrt-shrrt ... shrrt-shrrrt ...

On the whole I was making good progress. Several times the saw jumped out of the groove and scratched the skin, but that is to be expected during sawing.

Shrrt-Shrrt ... shrrt-shrrt ... shrrt-shrrrt ...

I got to the bone. The bone proved tougher, but then it started to give way too. Then the saw's blade got clogged up with some sticky dirt. I wiped it off with a finger and flicked the gunge into the loo. And got on with the sawing again. Muscles, tendons, bones – all gave way. My confidence grew. It turns out I am not all thumbs, as Auntie used to tell me. I smiled at the joke, which came to my mind unbidden. When the foot was nearly cut through I put away the saw and reached for the axe. With a few brisk chops I finally severed it from the leg. Stupidly, though, I was not holding it and the foot plopped into the toilet bowl. I cursed and delicately fished it out with two fingers. For a moment I hesitated whether I should wipe it dry so as not put a wet item in the stove, and even made a movement towards the towel, but laughed aloud at myself. I put the foot on the hot range in the kitchen and returned to sawing off another piece of leg. This time I was careful to avoid the embarrassment with the toilet bowl. At long last the foot and the other piece lay in front of the stove.

The heat inside the stove was wonderful. I threw in more pieces of paper and wood to build up the fire and chucked the foot into the shimmering void. It sizzled. I heard a hollow thump of the falling weight. The flames began to lick the new item. The skin began to blush and stretch. I smelled the odour of burning tallow. I was very tempted to watch the struggle of the flames with the corpse's foot a bit a longer, but overcame the temptation and closed the hatch. It could have led to some kind of unhealthy sadism, which so far had been absent in my relationship with the corpse. Anyway, the fire burnt better with the hatch shut.

Somehow I lost interest in preparing the cutlets now. There was still time, I told myself. And went to the room and lay on the bed. Like an old sybarite I took time to arrange the pillows under my head and shoulders, and to wrap myself in the blanket. I wanted to make my bed as soft and comfortable as possible. I reached out for a book. Oddly, it happened to be Dante's *Inferno*. I was irked by this theatricality, which from time to time emerged against my will and against – I was very much aware of that – my actual situation. But then, what was I to do if only this book was within the range of my hand? I didn't have much of a choice anyway. The few miserable books lying on my shelf were all so thumbed I had long lost any interest in them.

I immersed myself in reading but as I read I was becoming more and more aware that my eyes were running through Dante's stanzas mechanically, without taking in any meaning. I felt sleepy. It was eleven o'clock. Perfect time for a midmorning nap. And then, when the foot is burnt, I'll cook myself lunch. I unclasped my watchstrap and unbuckled my trouser belt. The room was cold. The fire, left unattended in favour of the kitchen stove, had died out. I wrapped myself tight in the blanket and closed my eyes. Sleep came soon after.

I woke up with a headache. My head was still full of images from my oppressive, suffocating dreams. I had dreamed a nightmare. I threw off the blanket and sat on the bed. Across the room hung a thin grey mist. And a smell of burning. I opened the window and leaned out into the frosty air of the street. My head swam. I turned back into the room and only then realised how it stank inside. Before I guessed the cause I was in the kitchen. It was dark. Thick black smoke and that sweet, sickly stench permeated the entire room. The stove looked like a volcano. Through the gaps in the range and the hatch door spewed heavy, lazy swirls.

I retreated and shut the door. The hall too was filling with smoke. I shut myself in my room and opened the window wide. Ugh, what an awful, sticky stink . . . I felt that stickiness everywhere: in my nose, on my hands, inside my mouth. I felt sick. I positioned myself by the window and taking deep breaths began to think through different ways of getting rid of the smoke. Alas, there was only one: air the flat. A dangerous way, attracting attention but . . . the only one. I held my breath and burst into the kitchen. I flung the window wide open and quickly ran back into my room, where the air was by now quite breathable. I wrapped myself in the blanket and covered my feet with a duvet. With my hands clasped over my chest, eyes fixed on the ceiling, I waited for the kitchen to clear. It was the method of an ostrich, perhaps, but who said I was to be constantly in a heroic mode of action? After all, so far the more energetic activity had always landed me in trouble.

But it was not granted that I should enjoy my peace for long. I heard banging on the kitchen door. A dilemma: should I open it or not open it? Of course – open it. I could not afford the risk of having someone break down the door and poke around my flat in search of the cause of fire. Behind the door rose a clamour of female voices. Someone started pummelling the door with a fist. I called out:

'I'm coming! I'm coming . . .' and turned the key.

I came face to face with a small group of frightened women. The poor ladies had abandoned their saucepans and hurried to my rescue. The corpulent Malinowska was holding a knife with which she'd presumably been cutting meat when she heard her close neighbour was in danger. Skinny, jumpy Benderowa dragged in her toddler; the look of terror in her irregular pale eyes made me want to laugh. But I stopped myself. The women swept me aside and ran in. They kept throwing questions at me, which fortunately I didn't have to answer as they were just as quickly answering them themselves, shouting over each other.

So I stood mumbling something, spreading my hands, smiling apologetically and thanking them. The women treated me with tender concern, putting into their words all the motherly affection they felt for those different twenty-year-old men – their lovers, husbands and sons – who were driving them to their graves. The energetic Piekarzowa knelt in front of the stove and began to fiddle about inside it with a poker. I offered my help and tried to take the poker out of her hands but was brusquely led away from the stove. It's not a job for boys. So I leaned against the sideboard and, talking to the ladies, waited for the half-burnt foot to fall out of the stove. Piekarzowa put the bucket to the hatch and with a few well-practised movements swept out a mound of ash. In a grey, acrid cloud of ash I saw the foot. It fell into the bucket. With a thud. Now Piekarzowa would look into the bucket and . . . I didn't want to imagine any more.

But nothing of the sort happened. The woman swept the stove clean and shut the hatch.

'Well, Mr Jurek,' she said, 'it won't smoke no more. And in the future – be careful.'

Nodding my head meekly I listened to warnings and indulgent rebukes. The kitchen was emptying. The women were returning to their kitchens. Only Piekarzowa stayed for a chat, asking me about Auntie and my dead parents. At length, she commiserated over my orphaned state and Auntie's toil – 'after all, an old person'.

At long last I managed to get rid of the ghastly woman. I sat down in the middle of the kitchen totally crushed. In front of the stove I noticed a piece of Auntie's leg still lying there. It was incomprehensible how they could not have seen it. I poked around the bucket and found the foot, charred but still retaining its natural shape. The good housewife missed that too. No doubt I was incredibly lucky, but somehow it didn't make me jump for joy. My lunch, which I prepared all by myself – the cutlets, so keenly anticipated by my taste buds – all went down the tube. And now the flat was cold as a doghouse. My first response was to take the foot with the ash and dispose of it in the rubbish bin outside. I knew it was risky but then it was already the second day and I still hadn't got rid of one piece of my deceased.

However, I refrained from that desperate step. Resigned, I picked up the foot and the piece of leg and carried them to the bathroom where I placed them on both sides of the corpse. Then from the sheets I selected the biggest one and covered the corpse as neatly as I could. Only one leg and the shorter stump were stuck out from under this improvised shroud.

The time of lectures approached. Having checked that the flat was more or less free of smoke I closed the windows and went out. I had my lunch in the corner bar. I chewed on bits of the over-seasoned stew but they only grew bigger in my mouth. I washed them down with a beer. It was flat and sour. I quickly paid the bill and went out onto the street. I checked my watch. It turned out I was about fifteen minutes early. These fifteen minutes would have to be killed loitering and window-shopping, or reading film posters hung outside the cinema on my way. I was not interested in the merchandise on display and I'd read the film posters several times before, but I stopped both before the shops and before the cinema. I didn't want to arrive too early.

The lecture was just like all the others I had attended so far. The cold barrenness of the walls and the ritual inventory hanging behind a framed glass on the door were exactly as they were before. I noted down some of the professor's words absentmindedly, though not more so than usual. His bony, short-sighted assistant was noting the professor's every word, turning his head in a funny way like a blind sparrowhawk. After forty-five minutes the professor put his coat on and went out for a fifteen-minute break. Then he returned and got on with his lecture for another three quarters. The assistant knew well when his moment would come and when the old man pulled out his watch he put his pen aside and waited in readiness. Then he jumped out, took the professor's coat off the coat hanger and, before the old man managed even to put it on properly, he was offering him hat and walking stick. It always went like this so I was not surprised by today's ceremony.

I nipped out for a fag. In the corridor by the window stood Alina, a girl with very bad legs, and vulgar Ewa, talking in a conspiratorial way, totally absorbed in each other. A few smoking boys gathered in a small noisy group. I caught fragments of some old crass joke which had ceased to amuse me when I was sixteen. Luckily, Mazan was not there. Instead another student came up to me and asked if I had managed to sort out something I was supposed to arrange for the party. I replied that I had not, yet, but that I would for sure. Because I was not inclined to keep up the conversation he soon left me in peace.

Nothing had changed here. My act, punishable by the gallows, appeared pointless and unimportant. That very same lecture hall, the dark corridor and the loneliness, which never left me among these people, whom I didn't need, who couldn't help me or even harm me. After the lectures I quickly sneaked outside. Yet, walking down the street I regretted my rashness. It was too early again. I couldn't think what to do with the evening. The flat was cold and I had no strength left to do any more burning. I slowed down, and then turned back towards the centre. Something was nagging me about the corpse at home, and the need to get back and do something about it. I ran in my mind through a short list of friends I could visit. Somehow I didn't feel like talking to any of them. But still, I kept walking.

I remembered it was a Saturday. I was definitely too young to spend a Saturday night moping around at home. Even a home shared with a corpse. I checked several cinemas but all of them had long queues. Dejected, I stood on the kerb and stared stupidly at the yellow splashes of electric light from the lamp posts reflected on the street and frozen puddles. Across the street I noticed two people I knew. They were students at the Academy of Fine Arts. Nice guys. With one of them I used to go to school; we even became friends. At first I wanted to turn and walk away. But then remembered I had nowhere to walk to. I quickly crossed the street and accosted them. We greeted each other in a noisy, friendly fashion. My friends were burdened with bottles of vodka and invited me enthusiastically to help them lighten their load.

I accepted. Immediately the mood turned light and warm. The conversation became noisy, punctuated with loud bursts of laughter. In Jacek's flat we found waiting for us two other boys and Hilda, a medical student. Hilda was wonderfully ugly, skinny as a pole and gracelessly tall. But she wore a funny little pigtail and could out-drink any boy. Without wasting time on spurious conversations we got down to it. It's hard to imagine a better place for drinking large amount of plain vodka than Jacek's room. It was very small yet oddly bleak. It had something of a station waiting room about it. The space between the wall and the wardrobe was crammed with rolls of canvas.

'Eat, take a bite.' Jacek invited us to rolls and sausage served on greasepaper.

So we ate and took bites. But most of all we drank. There were no glasses. We drank from heavy clay cups. Bottoms up. By the third round a great discussion broke loose about art, politics, philosophy and ethics. We spoke all at once, with great wit and passion. One of the boys, Janek . . . yes, Janek, picked up a guitar and started strumming it. We broke into a song. Personally, I had had enough, but the vodka had to be finished. The cups clacked again. One of the boys disappeared down the corridor and returned after a while rather pale and with wet hair. I felt I would soon follow suit. I was seeing drifting black clouds and felt a sweet acerbic taste in my mouth. Now people regularly disappeared behind the door, returned and drank on. Only Hilda didn't move, sitting ramrod straight throughout, though she drank the most.

We reached the point of soul-searching and confessions. Jacek put his arm around me and poured out his heart. He swore his undying friendship, pledged his life to creating great art and threatened to show someone what's what. Before long we were hugging and kissing. In the process we knocked the table and one of the cups fell on the floor. Next I was in someone else's arms. Again we hugged and opened our hearts. I had definitely had enough. I was burning with the fire of impatience. I got up and, swaying, headed for the coat-hanger.

'Jurek, where are you going?' Someone grabbed my arm.

'I'm going,' I mumbled. 'I must . . .'

Now more hands grabbed me and threw me on the bed. Everyone talked at me. A new cup of vodka was put under my nose. I leapt to my feet and turned over the table.

'Fools!' I screamed, 'I have a corpse at home! I'm a murderer! A murderer!'

With outstretched arms I tried to reach the door. Somewhere on the way I tripped over a stool and crashed to the floor. My head was booming just like a bath struck with an axe.

'I'm a murderer, ha ha ha!' I cried, picking myself off the floor.

'What are you doing?' shouted Jacek. 'Be quiet! Peasant . . .'

'Leave him alone,' said Hilda soberly. 'He's completely drunk.'

5

Walking down the street I saw double. I don't think I had ever experienced it before. I amused myself by guessing which of the twin objects was real. And usually got it right. But my trousers were wet from wading through imaginary puddles. I vomited lightly and without any difficulties. I was balancing on the pavement, courteously giving passers-by a wide berth. I was trying to sing, but my throat was dry and the voice came out raspy. I came to a little square with two lonely benches. I dragged myself to one of them and keeled over. Immediately everything around me began to sway. The stability of my position instantly released the dynamic volatility of the world. So I changed my position. I stretched out on the bench with my head hanging down and legs thrown over its back. The world viewed from this vantage point through the prism of alcohol seemed for the first few seconds quite interesting. But it didn't last long. I had to change my position again, as this one wasn't very comfortable. Handling carefully the absurd weight of my head I arranged my body into ever different figures. Now I sat on the armrest with raised arms. Then changed into an ape. Then into a hero. I blessed the alcohol, which allowed me to assume all those forms. Eventually I let go of the bench and moved on. I stopped for a moment and raised my finger:

'No one will learn about the corpse,' I whispered conspiratorially.

The tarmac on the street where I stood was glistening and looked slippery. I hesitated before stepping onto it like before stepping into a river. Suddenly I heard the drum of horses' hooves. In the perspective of the street loomed an ornamented coach pulled by two horses. I recognised a hearse. The horses ran at a trot and the hearse was approaching quickly. Enthralled and elated I opened out my arms.

'Oh, you drivers of death!' I greeted them. 'I envy you. And admire. Oh how I admire you. How lightly, blithely and gracefully you carry off death! While I . . . I'm tired of it, I – miserable murderer. Ah, why do I bother . . . I rejoice in your triumph. And thou, Cerberus with a peasant face – thou, that's right, thou . . .'

The hearse was almost level with me now and as I spat out the 'thou' I pointed my finger at the face of the coachman dressed in a funereal garb:

'Ha ha ha! Ride on, my hero. I shall farm my little bloody field myself. With the saw! With the axe! I kill . . . I kill . . .'

The hearse was vanishing in a whir of turning wheels and trotting hooves. I followed it with my eyes and said in a hollow voice:

'As old Goethe used to say, as old Goethe used to say . . .'

I moved on with my open arms. I felt strong and free. The annihilation of the corpse seemed an easy task again. The sense of power exhilarated me.

'I'm free through murder!' I cried out. 'Freeeeee!'

As soon as the words died on my lips I was arrested. I didn't even try to resist. Two militiamen held me fast in a way that precluded any attempt at breaking loose. I let them lead me away in peace and humility. I was trying to carry myself with dignity. Not to tremble, or rattle my teeth. I thought bitterly that my freedom didn't last long. Not even forty-eight hours after the terrible deed. How long is forty-eight hours? A day has twelve hours. Twelve and twelve.

I was intrigued by the forthcoming trial and being hanged. I didn't feel bad at all except for the paralysing fear of beating. I resolved to tell everything as soon as we arrived somewhere. I considered my chances of getting away with it. Very slim. Almost the entire corpse lay in my bath. Ah, but it probably lies there no more. They must have taken it away for the forensics. But then they may have left it there under guard – I wonder what he looks like, this man sitting in my flat now – and they will lead me to it. God, I hope they won't beat me. I could hardly control the trembling.

The vodka evaporated now. There was only fear left. I saw the neon letters on the police station. The duty room made a ghastly and sombre impression on me. The only light was a desk lamp, which had no lampshade and cast on the walls huge shadows of people and objects. I took in the drab furnishings: the desk behind a bar, two chairs, a scratched bench. It crossed my mind that in a few minutes I might be laying on that bench, naked, bleeding and trembling. And proudly I raised my head. Standing so, with my face like a mask, I tried to think of the scornful grimace I should adopt for the first question.

They pushed me towards the desk. I looked straight in the face of the duty sergeant behind the counter. It didn't make any impression on him. They took away my wallet, my trouser belt and shoelaces. Luckily my trousers hung well without the belt and I could still look a hero. The militiamen weren't showing any interest in my person, which hurt me. They just chatted among themselves sluggishly. I couldn't follow their conversation as the vodka began to swoosh in my head again. One of the militiamen, a weakling, shorter than me, which I found personally offensive, escorted me down a dark corridor to a heavy steel-clad door. The bolt clanged and I was pushed inside a cold, unlit cell.

I stood rooted to my spot. I didn't dare to make a move. I couldn't see a thing. From the corners of the cell came animal-like grunts. Slowly my eyes grew used to the darkness. I began to get a sense of the dwarfish proportions of the cell. But decided not to leave my spot. Suddenly I felt a live force grab me by the feet. Some enormous boa started winding itself around my legs. Roaring and choking I grasped at the wall. The pressure eased momentarily, only to squeeze itself tighter. A large, heavy body was performing some terrifying convolutions around my feet. I stood patient as a sea rock. Based on the alternating rhythm of pounding and panting I came to the conclusion that there were in fact two bodies. But I was not sure. The hand which leaned against the wall and with which I was supporting myself was beginning to throb with the effort. At long last the bodies let go of my feet and crawled away into deeps of the den.

With my back against the wall I slowly shuffled into a corner where I sat down. The worn-out drunks were now lying in a writhing heap in the opposite corner. I thought that for my crime I was to suffer not only through the interrogation and execution but also a Golgotha of humiliation. Reducing me to the level of drunks seemed to me particularly cruel. Their primitive noises kindled in me the fire of hatred. Meanwhile, having rested a bit, the pair resumed their orgiastic antics. I could now distinguish the movements of this creepy octopus. It wasn't howling now but purred in a monotonous, almost plaintive fashion, locked on the clay floor in a weird dance, accompanied by a hollow thumping. Suddenly the corridor echoed with steps. The drunks grew still. Through my body ran a funny shudder, all the way from my toes to the top end of my spine. I felt a touch of chill on my cheeks. I rearranged my legs in readiness to spring to my feet but waited with dignity. When the door opened I was ready. I didn't want to get up without an order.

The order didn't come. Instead a small, inconspicuous-looking man was pushed through the door, and the bolt clanged shut. There was nothing left to do but to kill time by observing the new arrival. The little man was sober. He looked around the cell without inhibition and said in a half voice:

'Blessed be the Lord.'

'*In secula seculorum*, amen,' I replied politely.

The drunks, feeling secure again, resumed their mumbling and writhing on the floor.

'May I take a pew with you?' asked the little man without moving from his spot.

'But of course,' I agreed.

He approached with a mincing step and sat down next to me. In the faint light from the street I could make out the rough outline of his features. The little man was probably coming to the end of his mature years. He had a small but fine figure, and a beautiful profile. Ah, how many Romans had I seen in the corner bar where I had my dinner. He didn't have a coat. His modest, threadbare attire hung on him faultlessly. He was, perhaps, the last earthly companion to treat me in a kindly, human fashion. So I looked at him closely. The little man was sitting still but I felt emanating from him manly energy and concentration. After a few minutes he turned to me:

'Do you think they will be able to understand my reasons?'

'I don't think they are capable of understanding anyone's reasons,' I said. 'Neither yours nor mine.'

'You are right,' he agreed. 'I will be taken for a relic thief.'

'Undoubtedly.'

'Funny, that,' smiled the relic thief. 'Consistent following of God's commandments always leads man astray . . . Were you surprised by my greeting everyone here?'

'No.'

'Excellent. I have nothing to say to people who are surprised by simple words. Such people bore me terribly. But it seems to me that you, sir, despite your tender age, have already acquired the wisdom of not being surprised by simple things.'

'Why do they take you for a relic thief?' I asked.

'Ah, this . . .' He smiled. ' I stole a golden arm.'

'From the Capuchin church? I know this golden arm well.'

'From the tone of your voice, sir, I conclude that you have lived in the New Town for a time and are familiar with the magic of the golden arm. I was troubled by it too, and more painfully than you, and for much longer. I'm twice your age. I'm forty-seven years old, nearly fifty.'

'The golden arm was, if I'm correct, given to the abbey in the seventeenth century.'

'Sixteenth. Your error is actually perfectly excusable, for it happened at the beginning of the Baroque period. In 1598 to be precise. Kazimierz Hermanowicz joined the order and the arm was kept in the abbey's treasury. Only after his death in 1610 was it put on public display, thus fixing the conviction that the arm was in fact given to the order in the seventeenth century.'

'Do you know other details connected with Hermanowicz?'

'Oh yes. The question of the golden arm has interested me for a long time. The moment I heard God's voice telling me to steal it, I began to study the matter in earnest.'

'Did you hear God's voice?'

'Huh, let's not simplify this . . .'

I didn't hear the rest of the relic thief's answer. The drunks, after a rest, burst out with their madness again. One of them snatched the other's belt with his teeth and now both were chewing on it, growling and tugging at it, each to himself. This tug of war went on for a while until an apocalyptic roar communicated to us that one of the drunks had lost his tooth. The thrashing on the floor stopped. Out came sobbing and words of succour. At last the two bodies rose and began to urinate in silence against the opposite wall.

'You were asking,' resumed my interlocutor, 'if I heard the voice of God. I think we should not pose this question this way. I am not a bigot who is having visions. God's will speaks to us without any metaphysical packaging. It simply manifests itself through certain decisions and thoughts in our brain. Through a certain order of events in our lives. I, my dear sir, have been dealing in sacrilegious thieving for a long time now. But they were mostly trifles.'

'Trifles?'

'Yes. Do you remember that little cherub with a porcelain head, nodding thanks every time someone put a coin in the box? He was my benefactor for two years. Every week I knelt before the box, sunk in prayer, during which I would pick the lock with a needle and take out the coins. I was caught by accident, in a silly way, as usual. Later I was involved in other sacrilegious thefts. Small votives, and once I had a go at a chalice. But a serious matter like the golden arm I hadn't tried before. It's a difficult case. It's possible I will rot for the rest of my life in jail.'

'Couldn't you try a psychiatrist?' I was worried I may have offended the sacrilegious thief but he showed no sign of taking offence.

'It's my only hope,' he replied gently, 'but whether it's going to be successful this time it remains to be seen. It's already helped me once, when I was put on trial for the chalice. I shammed it rather badly and they didn't believe me. Only when I started explaining the true philosophical motivation of my actions the doctor wrote out a certificate which saved me from five years of prison. I think now I have to go along similar lines. Tell the truth. Truth opens the gates of heaven. It's interesting how many people advocate following the teachings of Christ yet practically no one understands their true sense. So far it serves me well. They take me for a madman. And yet it's so childishly simple, like sunshine. Since God created the sacred, he had to create the sacrilegious. Since at the root of our religion lies the legend about a murder, it's natural the murderer have to exist. You killed a man . . .'

I shuddered. The sacrilegious thief didn't notice it and continued:

'In your case the primitive desire of enriching or exacting a revenge –'

'I didn't kill to enrich myself, or out of revenge,' I interrupted him.

'Oh, I'm sorry, I didn't mean to pry into your personal affairs,' the sacrilegious thief apologised politely.

I said in an unnaturally high voice:

'I simply killed.'

'That's OK too, young man,' my companion smiled gently, and then asked:

'Are you a believer? Please excuse the forthrightness of my question.'

'No.'

'I thought so. The youth of today is mostly unbelieving. Without unbelievers the church would not exist. But I do hope one day you will find your path to God.'

'It's very kind of you to wish me well,' I replied politely. 'Trouble is, I have very little time left to find that path.'

'Hm, true,' smiled the sacrilegious thief. 'But let us be of good faith.'

My conversation with this kind man absorbed me to such an extent that I didn't hear the steps in the corridor. When, pulled roughly by my sleeve, I was leaving the cell, my companion didn't even send me one parting look. In the other corner the two drunks were snoring away, soaked in urine and blood.

'Student . . . Yes. Very well . . . Which college?'

I gave the name of my university. The desk sergeant looked at me sternly and disapprovingly. The militiaman standing next to him smiled.

'A learned man,' he opined spitefully.

I was very ashamed. I stood humbly in my socks, holding up the falling trousers. They still had my shoes and the belt. There came a moment of weighty, contemptuous silence. I smiled differentially.

'Citizen officer,' I said. 'Saturday. It happens . . .' and opened my arms in a gesture of hopelessness.

The duty officer liked it. He didn't smile, but in his eyes flickered a quick humorous spark. He frowned and asked:

'How much did you blow yesterday?'

'I wasn't paying.'

'Hm.' The duty officer began to leaf through the papers and engaged in a conversation with the militiaman. It went on for ages.

I used every moment they turned away to arrange my face into a sneering grimace. Apart from the three of us there was also a young lady in a scarlet fur. She had come to the station to ask about her fiancé, a petty thief with whom she had spent the night. The woman was richly rouged, pretty and full of scorn. Her presence embarrassed me deeply. I felt deep shame in her presence, what with my dishevelment and the whole jail situation. She wasn't looking at me at all, which hurt me even more. At long last the duty officer finished his conversation, rose from his chair, put his hands in his pockets and began pacing the room. He stopped by the window and looked through the glass with calm concentration. Then he came up to the locker and took out my student's card, my belt and the shoes.

'Get dressed,' he said. 'I hope I won't see you here again.'

I wished that more fervently than he could ever guess.

6

The relief which filled me to the brim after leaving the police station, at home turned into depression. Sitting on the bed I ruminated on my merciless fate, which kept throwing me higgledy-piggledy into cruel, humiliating adventures. The thought that I had just brushed against the gallows, in fact slipped through the noose, didn't give me any satisfaction. I had made a fool of myself. Cringing and cursing myself I recalled the details of the past night. The memory of the drunken exploits at Jacek's pressed so heavily on my mind that even though I was already lying in a half-slumber, I extricated myself from the bedding and snatched my coat.

With pitiless stubbornness I was going over and over the infamous episodes, my childishness, my stupidity and my fall. And then suddenly – came the fear. I knew fear well. It had come to me several times in the last few days, hitting me with a greater or lesser force. The new attack was dangerous. I recalled with terrifying clarity how I had screamed at Jacek's: 'I'm a murderer!' How I drank, how I kept saying in the street: 'Now I'll cut her head off!' – moments before being stopped by the militiamen.

It was six in the morning. The hangman's hour. Shaking with cold and terror I lay fully dressed on the bed and pulled over myself all the bedclothes. But the calm wasn't coming. I leapt out of bed and with all my strength started slapping my face. In spite of my fainting, frozen body I threw off my jacket, sweater and shirt, and began to exercise vigorously. I tortured myself with sit-ups, press-ups and handstands, listening to my pounding heart and wheezing breath. I ran to the bathroom and put my head under the tap. Then started massaging myself with karate chops and kneading muscles till I felt pain. Then got dressed and went back to the kitchen. I put the kettle on the gas and made myself a cup of hot tea.

Gritting my teeth and determined I returned to the bathroom. The saw and the axe were already there. The fear had left, as always when I focused on a concrete job. I pulled the sheet off the corpse. Rolled my sleeves up. And began to saw the other leg. I used the tried method. First the foot, then the calf.

Shrrt-shrrt . . . shrrt-shrrt . . . shrrt-shrrt . . .

When I'd shortened the second leg just like the first one, I had a break. I allowed myself a cigarette. It was tasteless. I went back to work. With a few short blows of the axe I crushed both knees. I turned the top of the toilet seat into a workbench on which I laid out the axe, saw, and open penknife. Using these tools alternately I managed to disconnect the stumps from the rest of the body. Now the corpse lay in the bath comfortably. It occurred to me that I had made a terrible mistake in not bleeding the corpse while it was still warm. I would have a much easier job. But it was too late for regrets. With the penknife I cut through the dress on the torso and peeled it off bit by bit. Without disturbing the corpse I managed to bare it completely. I rolled the rags into a ball and stuffed it behind the kitchen stove.

That was all I could do with the corpse in this position. To proceed with severing the remaining limbs the corpse had to be repositioned. I thought about it for a while, then grabbed it under the arms and lifted it. The effort was killing me. Soon I felt hammers banging on my temples. The corpse began to put up resistance again. The lolling head just would not rest on the rim of the bath. I wasn't giving up though. With all my muscles strained to the limit I pulled up the corpse over the bath's edge. I gave it another pull and when the resting point came to about halfway down the back it finally kept its balance. I began to saw. I was trying to steer the saw away from the ribs so it cut only through the flesh. When I reached the spine my arms were numb and before my eyes floated black wispy blotches. But I didn't want to stop the work halfway through. I sawed on. The body began to quiver and tilt. I mobilised all my energies to keep it steady. At last the spine gave in. From then on it was all a breeze. I pushed the cut-up remains back into the bath.

The corpse ceased to be a whole. It lost its corporeal identity. Inside the bath lay the stomach and thighs, flanked by the breastbone at one end and knees on the other; on the tiled floor – an oddly proportioned bust with two large breasts, head and very long arms. I picked it up by the hands and threw this . . . shape into the bath. Then covered the flesh with a sheet. For it was flesh. Just flesh, not a corpse. Not even a carcass. My victory over the corpse was therefore only a victory over form. The body was still in the bath and not a tiniest piece of it had been annihilated. It was, if anything, a moral victory. More like capturing the enemy flag. The corpse had lost its flag.

The third day of my battle with the corpse was coming to an end. It should start decomposing now. In some warehouse I bought several kilos of crushed ice and laid it over the remains. On top of the bath I put down three small planks and on them a few of Auntie's plants. In the centre Auntie's collection of cacti, on the sides a tiny papyrus and an araucaria. The bathroom acquired a very pleasant ambience now. Something like a tranquil little chapel.

The following day I took out from under the sheet one of the remnants. At first I couldn't work out which part of the body it was. I was pleased with that. I wrapped it carefully in paper and tied it with a string. On the parcel I wrote an address. I had been thinking about this address for hours, rejecting the more eccentric ideas so as not to make it look too suspicious but trying to avoid banality or unwarranted carelessness. I opted for the surname ending in '-ski' but the combination of other letters was quite unusual and beautifully sonorous. I added some class to the popular name of Edward too by spelling it with a 'v'. And gave the sender the witty and laconic name of Antoni Nul.

The clerk at the post office cast a critical look over my parcel.

'What's in it?' he asked.

'Perishables,' I explained.

'Write it down. Besides, it's not tied properly. There . . . see?' he shook the parcel and the strings began to loosen up and slip off.

Contrite, I struggled with the string for a long time, then timidly asked for a bit of sealing wax, with which, in all that confusion, I burnt my fingers. At last the parcel was accepted.

After the lectures I bought a larger amount of string, carton boxes and paper. I prepared two types of ink, a pen and a sharpened stick. I spread out on the table a plan of the town and a map. I scoured the plan in search of streets with amusing or lyrical names and wrote them down. To my fictional addressees I gave names of characters from my favourite books. I had to give those names Polish forms, which was a lot of fun. I wrote alternately with a pen and the stick, and changed the inks. From time to time I also changed the style of writing, now making it look like the clumsy scrawls of an illiterate, at other times drawing straight lines with a stick. Then I remembered that among Auntie's few books there was a manual of calligraphy. The old little book after years of neglect was to be useful again. I practised studiously the old-fashioned flourishes, ruining three sheets of paper in the process, until I achieved a perfect example of the old school. As the hours passed I grew calmer and hopeful. When I fill those fifteen boxes and send them out I can proclaim victory.

At long last all the addresses were ready. I brought from the bathroom a piece of the body and started wrapping it up. Suddenly I stopped. I felt overcome by a wave of fatigue. And with it by fear. I was familiar with this condition. Whenever I got absorbed in some light task (heavy manual work was out of the question) after some time I began to feel a rising anxiety. It was a vague sense of terror, dejection and depression, which had only been temporarily tricked by my activity. Today the anxiety was more tangible and easier to overcome. If before I was simply unable to find a logical explanation of why I was engaged in reading a particular book or puzzling out a certain test, now finding a justification for my action was straightforward and irresistible. The battle with the corpse had liberated me from those unmanly histrionics and feebleness. It was the first difficult and dangerous task I had ever faced. Although the panic attacks still happened they had a real cause. I learned to overcome them through cold rationalisation of my current situation, from which followed the choice of appropriate actions. This time, though, the fear seemed to have been better grounded than usual. For once in some remote little town someone unpacks my parcel, some other one somewhere else will pin on his map a little flag on the dot denoting our town. The more parcels bearing stamps from my local post office are opened in various corners of the country, the more leads for our militiamen to conclude that the murder had taken place here rather than anywhere else. At the same time I was aware that the day I should inform the authorities of Auntie's disappearance was getting inexorably near. The date I will give them will have to coincide with the time of death, established in the course of forensic analysis of the remnants. And that will be suspicious, for sure.

It is possible – I reasoned with myself – that my thinking is full of holes due to my lack of experience, nevertheless it was undeniable that by sending the remnants by post I was giving the detectives a certain advantage. I felt disappointed. All that nice, calming work would be a waste of time. There was nothing for it but to tear up all the fictitious addresses, inventing which had been such a pleasant distraction; pleasant not only because it was fun but also because I believed it to be useful. Once again it crossed my mind that the annihilation of the corpse was harder than might be generally believed, that the struggle is tough and the adversary brave. So – what to do? I thought of the river. I had already been to check it. The banks were frozen, so a parcel would have to be thrown in away from the ice. But I wouldn't dare to drop it from the bridge, even in the middle of the night. Unless I packed it all away in a sack . . . Sack, I need to buy a sack. Come on – I was getting annoyed with myself – where does one buy a sack? I went in my mind through all the shops I knew, yet I could not remember a single one where they might be selling sacks. I gave up. I'm sure I'll find one. But then, who needs a sack? I'll take a few parcels and throw them in the river outside the town. I decided to go there tomorrow. Confidently I wrapped the piece lying on the table and put it in the box. Then started tearing up slowly the labels with fictitious addresses.

Still, the moment I tore up the first label, the doubts returned. I took the parcel out to the bathroom and stretched myself out on the bed. My experience with the corpse had taught me to avoid harried, unpremeditated actions. I thought that by giving the authorities the advantage in sending the parcels by post I could immediately turn this advantage . . . to my advantage. OK, tomorrow morning, at an anonymous post office, arrives my parcel bearing a stamp of our town. But what if another post office receives a parcel bearing a stamp of another town? And the day after tomorrow another parcel with another piece of the corpse will be stamped in another town altogether? Let's say they will eventually come to the conclusion that there is one murderer. But how will they decide which is his true address? Rather, they will assume that posting the parcels from different towns was a deliberate ploy. How could they tell that the murderer would start with his home town? Such a perfidious criminal should steer clear of any post office near his permanent address. Who knows, maybe it will be a dot without a flag that will come to be the focus of the investigation? I went on honing my plan. I rejected the idea of visiting several towns in a row. That would be too expensive. Moreover, what excuse would I give at the university for absenting myself from the lectures? Still, the advantage once handed over to the enemy should be immediately turned around. Tomorrow I shall take three parcels and post them from the main post office in a big town two hours away by train. That should be a big enough stick in the spokes of the investigation. The rest of the body I shall dispose of here by different methods.

From the pile of addresses on the table I picked out those which struck me as the funniest and returned to the packing. The overall weight of the parcels was 25 kilos. I took them out to the bathroom and burnt the rest of the papers with addresses.

7

Travelling had always held a certain attraction for me. In my modest experience I had travelled little and every trip – even the shortest – was for me a source of amusement and an adventure. In a different town I felt a bit like a foreigner. It was still before midday when I had all the parcels posted and so I went for a stroll around the town. Luckily, it was warm and sunny. Posting the parcels was a big step forward. Pleased with the progress I decided to spend the rest of my time in town on small pleasures. When I got tired walking the streets I stepped into a café. I treated myself to a big coffee and two cakes. I had my lunch in a good restaurant, choosing the menu with the sedulous care of a gourmet. After lunch I felt a little tired. My return train was in the evening. Wandering around I came across a cinema. They were showing a movie for which it was impossible to get tickets in my town, but here I bought one without trouble.

Movies make me vulnerable and leaving a cinema is almost always a nasty shock. The exotic glamour of a foreign town was shattered, showing all its fragility. The station was only dirty and noisy. Many times I promised myself to go to the cinema every day, to spend much of my time – I was afraid to say: life – in lethargy. I never fulfilled my promise.

The train compartment was not overcrowded. Opposite me

sat a girl reading a book. She was pretty. I was observing her with pleasure, the light auburn lock of hair on her forehead, a small nose, her dark, resolute eyebrows. She had delicate, shapely hands. With sadness I thought that soon she would leave the compartment and I'd stay behind alone with sleeping workers, or maybe she'd get off the train with me in our town, but then we'd lose each other in the crowd. Be that as it may, I would be left alone. Almost with gratitude I thought about my corpse, struggling with whom somehow filled my loneliness.

The train was moving at a sleepy pace. We were passing the scattered lights of villages and small towns. The light bulb hanging from the ceiling gave faint, murky light. How can she read? – I thought about the girl. And without any premeditated plan I said:

'You will damage your eyes.'

The girl quickly raised her head and frowned lightly. Then she smiled and put away her book.

'Thank you.' She smiled again. 'I'm used to it, they always tell me off for reading in the dark.'

'And quite rightly too,' I replied solemnly.

We started to chat. At first I was afraid that our light, casual conversation would suddenly break off after some trivial remark, that after a few stops, before we reached our town, we would fall silent, running out of things to say. But as we spoke the risk of it happening was fading away. We slowly relaxed into our chat and the moments of silence that fell from time to time between sentences did not separate us. We were silent together. At some point I felt the girl's hand on my knee. I appreciated the gesture but still didn't dare to touch her hand.

We were smoking cigarettes in the empty corridor. In the distance, far from the tracks, passed the lights of some settlement.

'When I was little,' said the girl, 'I believed that those lights are the lanterns of the elves. During the day the elves slept and no one knew about them. But at night they came out onto the hills and lit their lights. The oldest elf, their king, lit a red a lantern. Me and my brother were always looking for the red lantern of the king. Did you believe in elves?'

'Of course.'

'Your answer lacked conviction. I sense the irredeemable influence of a rationalistic upbringing.'

'But you are still very young.'

'Ah, you old men . . . I see you have acquired the arcane art of old-fashioned gallantry. Never mind, let's look for the red elf.'

'So far we haven't been very successful.'

'So what. The greater the effort, the sweeter the reward. Oh, look, there . . . the green one. He is also an important elf. Though he is far below the red king.'

'I understand that the kingdom of elves has its own bureaucratic hierarchy. I wonder who is in charge of the elven field workers?'

'Boring realist. It's clear you never believed in elves.'

'But I assure you, I did, but . . .'

'But?'

'But I stopped. I simply grew up and started thinking seriously about the future.'

'Very commendable.'

'Very. And by the way, I'd gladly give a big part of my life – I don't have any other capital – to someone who could convince me there is a future.'

'Hm, a Hamlet too.'

'Yes. A Hamlet. But unlike thousands of other native Hamlets, I have at my disposal a real skull.'

'Strongly put.'

'I'm sorry, I won't bore you any more.' Suddenly my spirits flagged.

'Hey, what's now . . .?'

'Nothing. Nothing worth talking about. '

'But why? We can talk. It's high time . . .'

I smiled bashfully.

'I'm very pleased we've met. I hope we will meet again.'

'Well, we live in hope.'

We stood in silence. I was focused, filled with blossoming joy.

'It's really great . . .' I mumbled out after a while.

'What?'

'That I've found the red elf!' I cried out, pointing quickly at a red light glowing in the distance.

We both burst out laughing.

8

It was a clear, starry night. I was returning from my date with Teresa. I walked with my head high, listening with pleasure to the sound of my steps echoing off the pavement. 'Teresa . . . Teresa' – sang my youth. Barely four days had passed from our first meeting and I was already riding the high crest of my love. With the submissiveness of weak character – which I'd been told I had – I allowed Teresa to take over all my thoughts and imagination. Even when I was thinking about other things somewhere through the back of my mind's eye passed the images of her face, her smile, her eyelashes with snow-flakes on them or her hands in old leather gloves, which had became a holy relic to me.

We saw each other every day. We both had no doubt it was love. 'Love, love' – I kept saying to myself aloud when alone in my flat. I hadn't neglected the corpse. Fortunately the cold weather held fast so the regularly replenished ice kept the body from decomposing. Only once during the last three days I wrapped up in paper some innards and discarded them on the suburban rubbish dump visited often by ravens and cats. That trip cost me a lot of time and effort and the result was rather measly. Once more I had to admit that the corpse was a tough opponent and fighting it requiring a lot of willpower, courage and ingenuity. I hadn't given it much time lately but I wanted to bring it to an end as soon as possible. It was getting bored with it.

I was slowly coming to the conclusion that the period when the struggle with the corpse filled the void in my life was over. The corpse was replaced by Teresa. Yet I could not accept this conclusion without reservations. I knew that a woman could not fulfil or replace all the various longings and desires that tore at my soul; I knew that nurturing my love for Teresa would mean killing it too. And yet, under the influence of this girl I was beginning to recover my faith in life. I knew it was an illusion, and I kept telling myself so. I had wasted too many years dreaming about the travelling, adventures and exciting life that awaited me. (Too many times I had been punished for my dreams by everyday objects in our flat, by the lecture hall, by all that machinery of terror which closed up on me, seemingly for ever.) Yet, when I was with Teresa I felt calm and believed, against all reason, that I was still destined for some great things.

These fanciful musings seemed to be backed up by my recent experiences. After all, killing Auntie and struggling with the corpse was definitely something. And my situation of a man standing between the gallows and an unknown adventure was not devoid of a certain dramatic grandeur. Nevertheless, it's not exactly the kind of drama I had in mind, not this kind of deed that Teresa's knight should be famous for. Such and similar thoughts crossed my mind in those days. Those thoughts and reflections were rather superfluous, unable to affect the great lightness that filled me. The attacks of fear still happened. I was aware that I was pushing my luck, dragging my feet about reporting to the militia while doing nothing about getting rid of the remnants.

In such moments my head would explode with brilliant ideas for annihilating the corpse. Once, as I was falling asleep with the image of Teresa under my eyelids, I was gripped by a spasm of fear. Any attempt to talk myself out of it and stay in bed were in vain. I dragged myself off the sheet and went into the kitchen. I rummaged through the sideboard and found the meat grinder. With some difficulty I clamped it to the edge of the table, picked out a few chops of dead meat and began to mince. My plan was terrifyingly simple, like that for a perpetuum mobile. I would mix the minced meat with the ash from the stove in the bucket and then take it out as usual in the morning and dump it in the rubbish bin. As I earnestly turned the crank the work – as it usually did – brought me peace. I thought of Teresa. Of our walks in the spring, which was just round the corner. Of alleys lined with young birch trees, of orchards, of those little white and yellow flowers which blossomed on the shrubs in spring. I was smiling and muttering to myself. Suddenly my bliss was shuttered by an excruciating pain. I'd caught my finger in the meat grinder. I yanked my hand out and put it to my mouth but dropped it immediately as the odour of the meat hit my nostrils. I picked up the crank again but without the previous enthusiasm. The work slowed down. The grinder was getting jammed. I gave up. I looked a picture of pathetic horror: standing in the middle of the night in my pyjamas with a bloody meat grinder in the cold kitchen. Now my brilliant idea seemed idiotic. My mind drifted over the question of how to disinfect the grinder. I threw the minced meat in the bucket and after some hesitation the other two pieces; after I stirred it all up, the ash covered the pieces so thoroughly they could not raise any suspicions. I went back to bed. The moment I closed my eyes the image of Teresa appeared before me to guide me into sleep.

I managed to get home just before the concierge locked the gate. I was pleased I didn't have to struggle with the massive rusty key. I ran up the steps and saw before my door two small human figures. The light shock gave place to amused annoyance. I recognised my granny and her daughter, Auntie's sister. They both lived in a small town in the mountains, a good dozen miles away from the railway station. Auntie, and what she sent them, was their only livelihood. Granny, who was nearly eighty, suffered some chronic pain in the ears and had them smeared with some iridescent white paste. It made her look like a strange bird. Seeing her, I always thought that if there were a biblical term for 'whitewashed tomb' – she would be it. Her daughter, a fifty-year-old virgin, was disabled and wore very thick glasses, without which she was practically blind. Apart from that she suffered from a serious stomach disorder, and played a violin. I remember a visit we paid them a few years ago in their home town. It was a warm September evening. Through an open window flowed a golden stream of sunshine. It was a golden, lyrical moment. Aunt Emilia stood by the window, hidden from the courtyard behind the curtain, and played. I can't remember the melody except that it was old and sad. When we entered the room she stopped and blushed like a schoolgirl. We had to plead with her for a long time to play something again. At long last, blushing and excusing herself, she agreed to repeat the concert. I remember vividly Granny's face beaming with almost lewd pleasure as she listened to the tones of the violin, and Auntie's – approving but unemotional. I remember that I hated her then. Who knows, maybe here I could find the roots of my deed, if I could be bothered at all.

I sat the old ladies down and began to lay the table. They both protested they would not eat, even though they were hungry and watched my every move heralding the imminent appearance of food with growing excitement. It amused me. I put the kettle on and made a pile of sandwiches. I used up all my cheese which was to last me three days. I worked quickly and with confidence. A week of self-reliance had taught me a lot. I told the women that Auntie had left for a long business trip and tried to assuage their worries about lack of letters and a postal order. When the supper was finally on the table the women rose to say a prayer. I got up too. Until now on these occasions I had always stood with my hands casually clasped behind my back with a blasé expression on my face. But the experience of the last few days cured me of my adolescent arrogance. I bowed my head lightly and clasped my hands in front of me. Towards the end I even made a vague gesture with my right hand. We sat down. The old girls ate with appetite. I excused myself and looked into the bathroom. The corpse was covered well. When the ladies began to yawn I made up the bed for them, and for myself laid a mattress on the kitchen floor. It was hard and uncomfortable.

'Oyey! Yey, yey!' I heard Aunt Emilia screaming in the bathroom.

I jumped up and switched the light on. Groping my way along the corridor I ran to see what happened. Aunt Emilia in her long nightdress was sitting in the bath with her feet high above her head. She was holding a lit candle in one hand while the other hand was making desperate waving movements.

'Who's here?' she stuttered out when I appeared in the doorway.

'It's me, Auntie,' I said as calmly as I could. 'What happened?'

Aunt Emilia started gibbering again.

'There is someone lying here . . .'

I got scared. Aunt Emilia had discovered the corpse. She should be killed. If I did it now, while she was still in the bath, I would spare myself the trouble of transporting her corpse. But then I'd have to kill Granny too. Three corpses on one head. No, that's too much. I took Aunt Emilia's hand and pulled her out of the bath.

'Someone's lying there,' she was shaking with horror. 'Jurek, dear, who is there?'

Trying to calm her, I carefully examined the bath. The depression indicated the place where the stomach and the lower part of the body lay. I knew the arrangement of my corpse very well and could determine precisely the position of each body part under the sheet. Falling in, Aunt Emilia landed on the best preserved part. She had mistaken the bath for the loo. She was still very upset.

'Someone is lying there . . . I think . . . I felt it . . .' she kept repeating.

I took the candle out of her hand and bent over the bath.

'But, Auntie,' I was explaining calmly, 'it's only linen. Look, there . . .' I carefully unfolded the sheet. I manipulated the candle in such a way that she could not see anything. Emilia was straining her sick eyes. She was calming down. Suddenly, when it seemed the danger was over, the light came on.

'Damn,' I cried out and raised my hand to my eyes as if blinded by the light. At the same time I pushed my elbow into her face, knocking off her glasses. 'Oh, I'm so sorry!'

The bathroom was flooded with light now. Aunt Emilia stood numb, rubbing her face. She couldn't see a thing. I took her gently by the arm and led her away to her bed. On our way we met Granny, who was woken up by the noise in the bathroom. She was wearing a white turban.

I fell into a heavy uncomfortable sleep, from which I soon woke up. Only now it struck me how much I'd grown used to sharing my loneliness with the corpse. The nocturnal presence of two old women in the house irritated and distracted me. I couldn't go back to sleep. In the surrounding silence I was picking out the slightest noise, barely audible squeaks of the furniture, the hollow, intermittent song of the kitchen tap. As my ears tuned in to those susurrations I could clearly distinguish the breathing of the two sleeping women despite being separated from them by two closed doors and a corridor. Then the breathing stopped and changed into whispers. I couldn't hear the words but the conversation grew louder, the beds squeaked and the room filled with a gentle bustle.

After a few moments I heard the clanking of plates and

cutlery. At first weak and timid, soon the clanking intensified until it sounded as if a noisy feast was under way in my room. Only the dinner conversation was missing. There were still some leftovers from the supper and the old girls were apparently clearing them off. When the bustle died down I heard the women tiptoeing towards the kitchen. As carefully as I could I rearranged myself on the mattress. I wanted to be able to observe them without arousing their suspicion. The women slipped into the kitchen and slowly approached my bed. Granny stretched out her hand and scratched me lightly on my nose. I didn't move. Then she whispered:

'He's sleeping, good boy . . .'

'God bless him,' said aunt Emily.

Assured, they turned away. The older led the younger, who in the dark probably couldn't see anything. They were heading for the sideboard but on their way bumped into the low, broad kitchen table on which I had left a bit of bread and sausage. They bent over the table and searched it thoroughly the way one looks for a lost ring in a meadow. They didn't reach for a bigger piece further away until they'd cleaned up all the crumbs before them. When the table was clean they moved on to the sideboard. The kitchen resounded with the music of feasting again. I knew that in the sideboard there was only a jar of marmalade, some sugar and a small bag of flour. The ladies consumed it all eagerly. Granny made little cakes of flour and marmalade, sprinkled them generously with sugar and fed them to her daughter. Herself, she ate them without sugar, protesting she didn't like them too sweet. When they got to the larder they were met with disappointment. The door was locked, the key hidden in an unknown place. I would have gladly got up and treated the old girls to all the food I had but was worried that catching them out on their greedy raid would embarrass them. So they stood hopelessly before the door, examining the empty keyhole. Aunt Emilia threw in the towel first:

'Let's go, Mummy. I'm not hungry now, really. Those cakes were very filling. Mummy . . .'

With reluctance Granny gave in, and both slipped out of the kitchen. I shuddered with disgust. The whole scene had looked funny, even moving, when I was watching it, but now when the women had left I felt nothing but deep revulsion. I promised to myself to send them away as soon as possible, by the earliest train, without sparing money or food for the road. I could not bear any more crawling around. I shut my eyes tight, pushed my head under the pillow and ordered myself to sleep.

I woke up early, filled with determination to get rid of the old girls no matter what the cost. I heard a melody and the words of a church hymn. Granny and Aunt Emilia pottered around the kitchen singing:

> *From the dawn*
> *Our souls*
> *Praise with song*
> *Maaariiiya . . .*

I lay quietly with my eyes shut. I felt snug and peaceful. I gently floated into the kingdom of childhood. Granny and Aunt Emilia pottering and singing. Daddy is not at home. Ah, how seldom I saw Daddy, and now Jurek, Jurus, Jureczek – he is in bed, napping. He is a child. His whole life before him. The whole world of unknown experiences, sensations and images, which were never come to pass. The women stopped singing and began to confer in whispers. I opened my eyes and raised my head.

'Good morning!' I said almost cheerfully.

Still in my underwear I entered the corridor. The bathroom door was opened. The sheet covering the corpse was pulled half way off. If the women discovered my crime . . . I was unable to finish thinking the thought. I bent over the corpse. On the right side I noticed a shallow but wide wound, as if

116

eaten out. There were other smaller wounds next to it, as well as scars and long scratches. It didn't look like the work of mice. I could not remember the presence of those animals in our house anyway. The window was shut properly, so an entry from outside, by a cat or a bird, was out of the question. The pest must have been already inside the flat. For a while I stood still with my hand raised in a half gesture, totally lost as to what gesture it should be. I bent over the corpse again and put my hand under the sheet. When I took it out it was holding Granny's false teeth. So, it was the girls – having been turned away from the larder's door, they had nibbled through the night at the cold rotting corpse. Poor things, they didn't have much of a meal. The flesh had been toughened by the ice. And getting it up from the bottom of the bath must have been hard work for them.

I stood turning Granny's teeth thoughtlessly in my hand, unable to decide how to deal with this new situation. Did they knew they were eating a corpse? Will it impair their weak health? Will they want to report me to the authorities? If they do I should kill them without delay – but what will I do with two new corpses when I can hardly cope with the old one? So, the old corpse again. It was clear that forgetting it was pure illusion. All the apparently unconnected incidents sooner or later led to the trouble with the corpse. I could lock the bathroom door and pretend the whole thing hadn't happened. But what to do with the teeth? Granny would certainly feel the loss of such a precious object very acutely.

At noon I escorted the women to the station. They said their goodbyes affectionately, even effusively. I found them seats in a compartment and helped with the suitcases. They left for starvation in a small mountain town. I gave them half of the money I had. I was consoling myself that with their thriftiness it should last them a good few months. At any rate, I calculated that I still had a few months before the next wave of desperate letters, telegrams, and then maybe another visit. By then

117

Auntie's disappearance should be officially accounted for. The thought of this official explanation was very unpleasant for me and I kept pushing it to the back of my mind.

9

In the evening I met with Teresa. In a corner of a cheap café we sat talking, delighted and joyful. Then we went for a long walk, wandering the streets. It was warm. In the air one could feel the breath of coming spring. We laughed a lot – at the lights in the puddles, the snowy lamp posts, fantastic silhouettes of old houses. Now and again I brushed my lips lightly against my girlfriend's cheek. We wandered into the cloister of a little old church. It was empty. Below flowed a noisy, sparkling street. At the crossing flashed a red light, tiny but clear. I thought: 'red elf', but didn't dare to say it aloud, afraid my voice would sound harsh under the vast dome of the sky. Teresa knew that too and whispered into my ear:

'Penny for your thoughts?'

The red light disappeared and the gesture of my hand towards it was late and pointless. I embraced Teresa and we started kissing. For the first time we felt the insufferable burden of clothes. We walked holding hands in silence, embarrassed by the fact that we still hadn't become lovers. We both knew that a lively conversation now would be a fraud. When we came to Teresa's house, she stopped.

'Go home, darling.'

'I'll walk you to the gate.'

'No, there's no need.'

'Why?'

'I don't want . . . You know what I mean.'

'Is it embarrassing?'

'Of course not. But what's the point?'

It was the third time we were having this conversation. Nevertheless we conducted it solemnly, repeating our lines without interrupting each other. The thought of going to bed alone, always an unpleasant one, today was simply terrifying.

'Yes, you are right, no point,' I said slowly and bent to kiss Teresa's hand.

I headed home but when I looked back and saw Teresa's small figure disappearing in the distance I turned around and ran after her.

'Teresa,' I said. 'Teresa, come with me.'

Without a word Teresa slipped her arm under mine and firmly took my hand. She was serious and calm. Feeling consecrated, almost canonised by our love and our decision, we got on the tram. Now and again, behind the rooftops, we saw the moon racing along. We were focused and silent. Only once, when I smiled at my girl, Teresa quickly put my hand to her lips. Our short journey along familiar streets, the elopement from a tram platform paid for with a discounted student fare, all that was so strangely beautiful I couldn't find any room to think or feel anything else but the thrill of flight filling my soul to the brim.

Only when we got off the tram, I began to worry. The remnants were covered well and I was not unduly worried that Teresa might discover them, even when she wanted to use the bathroom. I was more afraid that Teresa would start asking me the questions usually asked by a new friend on a first visit, and force me to tell lies. Until now, when the conversation had drifted onto domestic arrangements, I'd offered some generalities and changed the subject. Teresa was too much in love and too happy to notice anything. Still, I remembered those petty lies and felt oddly distraught by them. Climbing the badly lit and dirty stairs filled us with cold. But finally . . . we were alone.

We sat on the bed in the murky light of a small lamp. I looked for Teresa's hand. She leaned against my shoulder and lowered her head. She was waiting for a kiss. The seeming ease with which I could continue this simple game, the conducive atmosphere and the surroundings, began to make me feel uncomfortable. Teresa noticed it and became gentle and protective. I wanted to tell her to go away, that she couldn't even guess how I was deceiving her, but instead I kissed her. When our embraces grew longer and more ardent my fear and scruples receded. I surrendered to the caresses with the full inertia of my senses and will. Everything else, the whole bloody business, became so irrelevant and distant that talking about it now would have been simply rude.

I woke up early. Teresa was still asleep. The room was filled with the grey light of dawn. I sat up in bed and felt cold. We were both naked. The night, during which I was heroic and tender, lascivious and exalted – had passed. Teresa looked unattractive. Her mouth was open. I got up and walked up to the washbasin. Took the mirror off the nail and looked at myself for long time. Then cast a sweeping glance across the room, and my eyes stopped on Teresa. I burst into tears. My body was convulsed with sobbing. I tried to suppress it. I pressed my lips, rubbed my eyes – nothing helped. I poured water into the basin and began splashing it over my face and shoulders, crying. I deliberately made a lot of noise, trying to drown the sobs, while worrying I might wake up Teresa. But she slept soundly. At last I dried my face with a towel and began to dress, looking for clothes and stifling the last spasms.

When I returned from the bathroom fully dressed, Teresa had already got up and put on her dress. I greeted her with a joyful smile. We exchanged a few words. Smoking my cigarette, I observed Teresa brushing her hair before the mirror. The morning dishevelment added to her charm. The beauty of youth, which needed no adornments, moved me deeply. Suddenly I was gripped by another attack of crying. Dressed, with shoes on, holding a cigarette in my fingers, I threw myself on the bed, weeping. The killing gave me my tears back. Teresa put away the comb and crouched by my knees.

'What is it, love? What is it?'

I could not calm down. Wiping the tears away, I was trying to take a puff on my cigarette, but with every attempt only more tears fell on my sweater. Teresa sat next to me and rocked my head in her arms. I was slowly calming down, listening to the gentle murmur of her words, feeling the warmth of her hands on my face. I felt better. I cried out all my tears which I'd hoarded inside for all those long years. And again I felt unable to cry. I pushed Teresa gently away and sat opposite her.

'Listen,' I began. 'I've been meaning to tell you something, something I must tell you. I must, even if you will hate me for it, or even destroy me.' I noticed on her face an expression of sympathetic understanding, which confused me. 'I have to ask you first however,' I continued in a quiet, serious tone – 'don't interrupt me. I want to tell you this because I love you, and because I feel you are the only person I want to tell it to.'

Slowly, choosing my words carefully, I told her everything, starting with a broad sketch of my relationship with Auntie and a discussion of the complex I had developed about her, feeling totally dependent on her, despite being younger and stronger . . . The rest I limited to facts. I was afraid I might lose my calm, raise my voice and begin to gesticulate. But I managed to control myself and continued in an even, matter-of-fact tone of voice. When I finished, after a long moment of silence, Teresa asked me:

'Is that all what you had to tell me?'

I nodded, but then immediately shook my head vigorously.

'No, no . . . I mean, don't worry, I don't have any more sins to confess. But I'd like to tell you so much more, so much . . .' I mumbled on.

Teresa got up and started putting her coat on. She walked past me as if I weren't there. Her indifference stunned me and got me shaking again.

'Teresa,' I pleaded with her. 'Say something . . . You owe me some explanation, don't you think? What do you think about it?' I stammered out hopelessly.

Teresa wasn't paying any attention. She seemed to focus her mind exclusively on simple things like closing her handbag and putting her kerchief on, the way I did when lighting the stove and preparing my first lonely breakfast. She started walking towards the door. I followed her and barred her way.

'Let me out,' she said, 'unless you are planning another . . .' Her eyes were hard and fearless.

'Go then,' I said slowly without moving. 'Go, and later, after they've hanged me, you can boast to your girlfriends that you slept with a murderer.'

Before I finished saying the last word she slapped me hard on the face.

'You have no right to hit me,' I continued in the same tone. 'If you want to, all you need to do is to say a word to those who can do it much better than you. No need to get offended. Sooner or later, you'll have to decide what you are going to do with it. One can let go and forget all kinds of rubbish and trifles. But you – you cannot even forget the red elf.'

The last words I said quietly and feebly. I didn't mean to be cynical. I had lost all my cynicism a long time ago. I carried on, tired and dejected.

'That is why you have no reason to take offence. Perhaps it was churlish of me to say what I said, but you cannot deny there was some truth to it. You are not, as far as I know, prudish or devoid of a sense of humour. Your attitude is that of a woman who is open-minded and possesses a high dose of intelligence. And a touch of exaltation. All these traits indicate that such a person could – one day – confide – not in everyone, of course – but confide quite light-heartedly . . . you know . . . what I told you. I wouldn't blame you, just like I would not blame anyone for anything, and not because I don't – in my present situation – have the right, but because I'm not convinced there is such a right. I think – simply – that we are all guilty.'

Teresa knitted her eyebrows and listened.

'And you don't know, you simply don't know . . .' I was beginning to lose the thread. 'Telling you all this, I'm trying to spare you the . . . so that . . .' I completely lost it. 'Teresa. Do you understand? Thousands of days, thousands of hours, during which nothing ever happens: the staple diet of my childhood and adolescence. The dreams that turn out to be just as empty. Or worse – they turn out to be a poison which kills any chance of a healthy vegetation. Were we fed the stories of valiant kings, knights and other heroes – just to vegetate? Why have I been condemned to vegetation? Who is to blame for it? Who?'

I began to pace the room. Talking gave me pleasure. Listening to the flow of my words, helping myself with gestures and seeing interest on Teresa's face, I felt, almost subconsciously, how much I loved myself. Humiliated and ridiculous, I abandoned myself, the crucified fool, to a desperate gesture. I do not intend to justify my crime with the commonness of crime in our times. The fact that we all, day after day, gouge eyes, break arms and hearts, that we all hide corpses in our homes, does not excuse me from a rightful punishment. We do not accept any other justice and the blindness of this one we know only too well. I do not mean to defend myself. If only because I do not feel guilty.

'It's terrible, but I understand you, and agree with you,' said Teresa. 'It's terrible.'

'Today I could think that you need my help, you – my red elf,' I continued broodingly. 'But that would be misleading. I love you, Teresa, and our time together is the brightest in my whole life. But beyond that? Do you remember, darling, we talked about it – that it cannot last for ever? For ultimately, what choice do we have? Marriage, legally sanctioned or not, or breaking up. And again the torture of boredom. It's just as well that with all that bloody business we still could be lovers.'

123

Teresa frowned and asked, rather concerned now:

'Very well, but what can we do with it?'

'With what?' I asked confused.

'You know, with . . . with Auntie.'

'We'll clean it up somehow,' I said absentmindedly, and suddenly we both burst out laughing.

The exhilaration of the previous evening, the rapture of the last night, the despair of the morning and the horror of the last hour – this whole concoction of moods exploded with our young, healthy laughter. The solemn discussion in which I was putting on professorial airs could not have ended in any other way. We laughed like kids. Every time we stopped and one of us tried to say something, it was enough to look at each other and the intended words were blown off our lips by laughter. At last, completely worn out, we fell silent. Teresa looked at the watch.

'It's late. I have to go.'

'Stay a bit longer.'

'I can't. I'm famished.'

'Excellent. We'll have breakfast in town.'

'Excellent.'

'You are a darling that you are not talking about home, where they must be very worried about you now.'

'I said I would stay the night at my friend's. And that is how it was going to be, if you hadn't seduced the homeless maid . . .'

Laughing again we left for the town.

10

The honey days passed for us under the sign of the corpse. Going to the bathroom Teresa dutifully ignored the bath with the cut-up remains. I forbade her strictly to look under the sheet. Teresa was obedient. Her participation in the crime still had for her the charm of novelty. She followed devotedly the unwritten code of criminals. Her attitude towards me had changed into boundless adoration.

'I want to serve you, serve you,' she would often say.

My attachment to her grew with every day. Ever hour spent without Teresa was difficult. I could not imagine my life without our moments together, without our discussions, dreams and pleasures. When the fear struck, Teresa brought me calm.

'My little one,' she would say, stroking my hair. 'My poor little one. Don't worry. Don't worry, I'm with you.'

'Who are you?' I'd ask with my eyes closed. 'Teresa?'

'I'm your girl. Your red elf.'

'Red? Why red?' I would tease her.

'That's the colour of the king of elves.'

'Tell me about the king of elves.'

Sometimes we would make plans for the future. Teresa, under the spell of the uniqueness of our situation, believed everything was possible. We fixed the date of our escape and determined picturesque routes for our travels. Those talks worked on me like opium. The reality of our situation seemed to me a trivial barrier which could be blown out of our way with a puff.

On Sunday we decided to go for an excursion out of town and drown in the river under the ice floes two little parcels of the corpse. At first I didn't want to agree to that.

'It's too risky, darling. It's my problem.'

'I thought you've understood by now that there are no your problems or mine – only ours,' she answered contrarily. 'But if you haven't understood – tough.'

'But Teresa, you know the situation, I'm not hiding anything from you. I simply don't want us to go out on our first spring walk with such a cumbersome baggage.'

'It would have been more cumbersome and unpleasant if you were to do it on your own. Isn't that so, my little one?'

'Yes, but do I have the right to put that burden on your shoulders?'

'It's like our baby. A consequence of me being with you.'

On Sunday morning, some time after eleven, we got off a bus at the edge of a wood. Springtime and blue skies were all around us. The paths were dry but the fields shimmered under a spread of snow. We squinted our eyes against the sun.

'Isn't that parcel too heavy for you, darling?' I asked.

'No, my little one, it's not.'

'Come on, let me carry it for you.'

'Certainly not. You carry the heavier one anyway.'

'That's OK, but you are a woman. I should carry you in my arms – not make you carry parcels.'

'The times we live in, eh?'

'You teaser, you,' I laughed and put my arm around Teresa. She looked into my face, her eyes burning with fire.

'Ah, my little one, I'm so happy.'

We put our parcels on the ground and began to kiss.

'Someone's coming,' said Teresa suddenly. 'Stop it.'

We saw a man approaching slowly from the fields, carrying a gun. We picked up our parcels and walked on. The official cap of the forester reminded me of things I would rather forget today. Teresa noticed the change in my face.

'Why so sad, my little one?'

'Oh, it's nothing, nothing really,' I replied, and then added sternly. 'Don't look at the sun.'

'Because?'

'Because you will damage your eyes, madame.'

'What? Ah, madame will damage her eyes . . . Oh, my little one.'

At the edge of the wood stood the yellow, ungainly building of an inn. We were the only customers there, except for a coachman in a padded work jacket drinking beer at the bar. Whenever I'd passed the inn before, the iron grille on its door was always shut. To this day it remains a mystery to me why it was open on that April Sunday. We sat down by the window from which spread a panorama of the surrounding wooded hills. We put our parcels on the empty chairs. After a while we were approached by a boy in a dirty apron and a face showing all the signs that we had disturbed his peace. After some protracted negotiations he agreed to bring us sausages and tea. We ate with the appetite of field trippers, joking and laughing. When we finished our teas, we lit up our cigarettes. The sky began to turn grey. Warmed and tired we were looking at each other's faces and hands, which reminded us of our pleasures. We knew it was a beautiful moment. The grey mist clinging to the treetops invited a mood for longing and dreaming. So I began:

'You may not know it, darling, but my father lives in Buenos Aires.'

'In Buenos Aires? And you never told me?'

'I'm telling you now. He lives in Buenos Aires and is a very rich man. The only problem is how to get there. Do you think it's impossible?'

'I don't know, love,' said Teresa softly, 'but since I met you nothing is impossible for me. Before I met you I had never believed in any possibility of changing my fate. And truth to tell, I never thought of it. But now, when I'm involved in such an extraordinary affair . . . It is extraordinary, isn't it, love? But maybe I'm hurting you, talking about it?'

I didn't reply. My eyes fixed on the horizon, I sat in silence, deeply moved and happy. Teresa's father was a forester and she spent her childhood and teenage years among the woods and lakes. Her first steps were blessed by the purity of nature, just as mine were cursed by neurosis. My longing for the forests and animals, stifled by the years of misery, and forgotten in the recent days of the struggle with the corpse – now began to stir inside me uncomfortably. Many times I tried to see it in the cold light of reason, that it was all a question of love, that I should focus on happiness, for Teresa loved me too. Indeed I had many moments of true happiness, yet I could not free my mind from anguish. And it would not be so bad if it weren't for the matter of my corpse. I knew that hiding it from Teresa I was deceiving her, and it hurt me. I could try and summon all my strength and remove the rest of the remains. But I had no strength left. Teresa competed with the corpse, and won. Over the last few days I hadn't undertaken any actions, only once slipping out at night with a small package wrapped in a newspaper and discarding the contents on a rubbish dump frequented by cats and crows. I felt burdened by the corpse like a man burdened with a family of whose existence he doesn't dare to tell his mistress, while his inherent decency prevents him from shedding the burden. Even in the happiest moments, when walking with Teresa through empty fields, joyful and light-hearted, bursting with unsuppressible laughter, so inextricably connected with our love, I carried the thought in my mind, which would suddenly flash like a signal – the corpse.

After a while I continued without looking at Teresa:

'I know a sea captain in Szczecin. A good man. When I was a child he used to carry me in his arms. An old, trusted family friend. I've learnt he works now on a regular line to South America. Will you come with me?'

'Ah, Jerzy . . .' Teresa stroked my hands with her fingertips.

Quietly, in low voices, we began to plot our escape. We refrained from showing any excitement in anticipation of all those exotic places we were going to see. No feverish discussions, no falling for the thrill of planning. We spoke in a calm, factual manner. I was deliberately pointing to the difficulties piling up before us, while slyly slipping in suggestions of how to overcome them. Teresa pondered them, knitting her brow, returning her opinion in slow, measured words. When at last we reached a contended silence, she said:

'Sometimes, when you are not with me, I feel you do not exist at all. I'm sure that in a few hours I'll think this conversation is a dream. And yet you do. I'm touching your skin and hair. My boy, my lover. You've put too much meaning into my life.

Sometimes I feel it overwhelms me. But I know you cannot be any other way. I don't think I would love you otherwise, if you weren't full of all those mysteries, of which I still know nothing.'

I squeezed Teresa's hand. She cheered me up. I felt like a good man. I gave a girl more than she expected. I made her happy the way I once made happy that old Capuchin priest in an empty church.

'Do you want to be with me?' I asked.

'I do.'

We threw the parcels into the river from a high, overgrown bank. We didn't discuss their contents. Only on our way back through the wood Teresa asked me, a little concerned:

'Darling, what was in my parcel?'

'Well, you know, surely . . .'

'Yes, but . . . which part?'

I remained silent.

'Come on, tell me. The leg?'

'Of course not, the leg would have been much heavier.'

'I'm not saying it was the whole leg . . .'

'Teresa, stop it.'

'You are right. I'm sorry.'

She quickly lifted my hand to her lips. We sat down on logs stacked in a clearing. Teresa took out two rolls, and offered me one. Leaning on a log I was contemplating the clouds drifting over the treetops.

'You know what, Elfi?'

'What, love?'

'Tomorrow is my national defence class again.'

'Poor thing, I'm scared.'

'Why?'

'I'm always scared before a defence class.'

'Don't worry. It won't be for long now.'

'What makes you think it won't be for long?'

'I'm sure of it, my little one. Before I met you I didn't believe my life could change in any way. And I accepted that. In fact, it never bothered me much. But now, when I'm involved in such an extraordinary affair . . . Just think, Jerzy, it's amazing . . .' She fell silent and having thought for a while, she added with conviction: 'I just know that everything will turn out as you want it.'

I waved my hand wearily. I knew that Teresa didn't really understand any of it. But her optimism and unbounded faith in me began to disturb me. When we plotted our escape, planned our travels and other adventures, I usually put forward the most bizarre, fantastic ideas. I could even find logical arguments for them. And the down-to-earth, practical Teresa fell for my fancy nonsense. As long as we believed in it together, it was all very nice. But now it struck me what an enormous distance separated me from those moments. Did it mean I was bored with love? Probably not. I needed Teresa, I wouldn't want to lose her. Yet I realised with absolute clarity that the only real thing was the corpse, at once a millstone around my neck and my lifeline.

11

I checked the timetable and realised the better option would be to return by bus. Any other time I would be disappointed, but today the prospect almost pleased me. I was disappointed by the Other Town. I tried to shorten the wait for the departure by discovering something special about buses. Unfortunately I could not find anything special. Their shape and yellow headlamps just didn't fit into any metaphor, they were horrifying. But only in their objective existence. I turned my eyes to the station clock, hoping this poetic object might retain something of the fairy tale I had expected from the Other Town. I looked at it intensely, lingering on the bright little star at the top. Still, I felt I was slipping back, despite putting into the effort all my imagination and all my intelligence. Suddenly

I heard the characteristic blare of the horn and at the same time, maybe a little earlier, a young voice:

'Careful!'

Someone yanked my arm. I let the pull drag me back. A few centimetres in front of my eyes passed a bus. I turned around towards my rescuer and recognised the Girl I Used to See. Before I could get my bearings and get out of the danger's way – I stood in the middle of the road used by the buses returning to the terminal – I had already grasped the meaning of this laconic message. Not for the first time the Girl interrupted my most carefully laid plans of suicide, which only returned later with double force.

I took my seat by the window and tried to adopt a position which would allow me to spend the long journey in the best possible comfort. I focused my mind on that. As the driver switched the engine on, someone sat next to me. I turned my head automatically. It was the Girl I Used to See. I shuddered. I turned my head away and fixed my eyes on the window. This situation required some reaction on my part. I was trying to persuade myself that fate had graciously given me a chance. But then I knew I could not take it, and felt rather ungrateful towards my fate. In the end I reached a compromise that best suited my mixed feelings: by observing the Girl I would destroy the myth of her Otherness, which in the meantime I had cultivated in my mind. Until now, almost always, I had seen her from a distance. Now that my face was practically next to hers, I should discover how common she really was.

I was observing the Girl closely. Pretending to stare absentmindedly through the window I studied her reflection in the windowpane, her profile, her hands; I was looking for signs of weariness in her face, which would make her just like the other passengers. After a while I could conclude with satisfaction that the Girl was tired; she even yawned once. And yet I felt defeated. The Girl still managed to retain the mystery of the previous encounters. The distance I felt then did not diminish now, when our shoulders pressed against each other in the shared misery of fellow passengers. Her remoteness could only be humiliated by talking to her directly. At first I thought of starting a casual conversation in the course of which I would defeat her apparent unavailability. Except that I was not really sure the victory would be mine. After all, talking to strangers had never been my forte. I cursed the situation forcing me to do this. At that moment it was no longer just a question of destroying her myth but of wasting the chance – the chance, which I had already forfeited. I was not afraid of embarrassment. I was simply too lazy to undertake such a great effort. The thought of having an empty flat at my disposal disarmed me completely. And yet I was not ready to surrender. I could only console myself that in a couple of hours we would reach Our Town and the Girl would disappear round a corner of some street. That thought actually hurt. I was counting the short stops, each of which was bringing this moment closer, inexorably. Suddenly I heard a loud crash and the bus ground to a halt.

The driver jumped out of his cabin and after a short while shouted something. Slowly, people started to leave the bus. I got moving too. The driver and the conductor were walking around the bus with their torches. It looked like something serious. Passengers complained and murmured among themselves. They looked like a lost herd of sheep; the sight cheered me up a little. We all stood by the roadside, close to the bus. Almost all the men lit up cigarettes. I looked around thoughtlessly and suddenly saw a slender figure marching down the road with light, confident strides. It took me a while to realise it was her. The Girl's movement were so strikingly different from the rest of the passengers', showing no sign of nervous impatience about the delay. It was hard to believe she belonged to the mass of commuters shuttling between the towns. The moon had just lit the road, there was no danger of me losing sight of her again. Some people began to walk around in small circles, as if locked in an invisible cage. Others took advantage of the bushes on both side of the road.

I joined the walkers for a while and then broke away to follow the Girl. We left the bus far behind. The Girl marched on, her pace steady and purposeful, as if she knew exactly where she was going. We passed a wooden building, then a birch tree. Then the road began to rise. I expected that once the Girl reached the top of the hill she would turn around and start coming down. I stepped out of the shaft of light and on to the side. But she marched on. For a moment I even lost sight of her. I hurried up a little. I began to enjoy this. Suddenly I heard a blare. Its muffled sound confirmed we had covered quite a distance. Then another blare. After a while I heard a quiet purr of the engine. The Girl stopped and spread out her arms undecidedly. For a few seconds she stood still, as if struck by the moonlight. Then she slowly lowered her arms and just as undecidedly turned around. At first she walked slowly, like someone out for a stroll, then she broke into a run. I stepped out of the dark and walked towards her. As she passed me by I said:

'The bus is gone.'

She stopped dead in her tracks. She looked at me carefully, without fear, and asked sharply:

'Who are you?'

'Aah . . . mm,' I began to stutter. At first I wanted to say – 'A murderer', for at that moment that was the most important thing about me. But I bit my tongue.

'A passenger,' I said at last.

We began to walk slowly, following the direction in which our bus disappeared. We walked, gathering pace, without looking at each other. The icy winter road like a belt drive carrying us forward, the white downy fields, clusters of houses and lonely trees marked the rhythm of our march. The moonlight shone all the time. Now and again a hare skipped across the road. I was getting tired. The march, at first a relief from the murderous seat on the bus, was now beginning to turn into another torture. Slight, niggling discomforts in my shoes and clothes grew harder and more painful with every step. My feet began to slip. I stole a glance at my companion, wondering if she too had reached the point of exhaustion. But the Girl's clear face seemed just as untroubled as it was on the bus. I had no idea how far was Our Town, or whether it was at all possible to get there on foot. Several times I wanted to ask the Girl but I couldn't bring myself to do it, fearing such questions were ridiculous against the merciless pace of our march, the road, the moonlight and the monotony of the landscape. When we passed the fourth village the road turned into the woods.

A high pine copse was quickly getting thicker, with more firs and naked deciduous trees. The moonlight began to disappear. I felt for the Girl's hand but found only the off-putting coarse sleeve of her coat and quickly withdrew my hand. Suddenly the Girl turned and, having jumped over a ditch, stood on a high path winding among the firs. With some hesitation I followed the Girl. Seeing me undecided, the Girl beckoned and said:

'Come.'

Or maybe she didn't say anything? We followed a slippery path, full of potholes and roots. I watched my step but at some point I lost my balance and fell. The Girl stopped abruptly and when I quickly picked myself up, we moved on. At last we came to a small clearing, silvered and sheltered on all sides. The Girl turned to me and said:

'We'll rest here.'

I didn't quite know how to behave in this situation. I looked around the clearing and hesitantly reached for my coat's buttons, wondering if I should take it off and spread it somewhere out on the snow. But the Girl started rummaging among the low firs, bent low and ferreting swiftly under the branches like a small tornado. After a while she returned with an armful of fir-wood.

'Help me,' se said. 'Here, hold it. Here . . .'

Obediently I took hold of two sharp branches.

'Now here,' ordered the Girl. 'Good.'

Soon I was working like a well-trained assistant, eagerly taking the prickly branches from her hands. The Girl was not slowing down. She no longer spoke to me, only with an eyebrow or a grimace praised my diligence or criticised my sluggishness. Before long we had a thick mat. I don't know how long it took us to build our fir hut; at any rate I had to admit it was very warm and comfortable. Half-lying on the hard fir mattresses we warmed up by the fire lit in the centre of our camp. I stood up my collar and stuck my hands inside the sleeves, worried that the warmth of the fire would prove illusory and the cold would start to bite. I needn't. Our little house was getting warmer and warmer. I was soon sweating like on a hot July day. Above the trees flew a sudden gust of wind. I could see thick trunks swaying a few metres away from our fire but here it was warm like in an overheated room.

The Girl took her coat off and kerchief, yawned, and began unlacing her boots. She got up and slipped them off without using her hands, just her feet. I noticed, surprised that our hut, although so cosy, was nevertheless high enough for a grown-up woman to stand comfortably inside it. The Girl took off her trousers and sweater and lay down, wrapping herself in her coat. I was looking at it in silence, swaddled in my own winter coat with its standing collar and the earflaps of my skiing hat lowered. The Girl wriggled for a while on her bed, then got up and moved closer. She took my face in her hands and suddenly kissed me on the mouth.

I stretched my arms and embraced her. She started to pull away, laughing in a metallic, sinister way. Entangled in my coat I couldn't decide if I should take off my gloves and my helmet-like hat, or hold tight to my trophy which was slipping out of my hands. The Girl helped me. She sat close to me and stroked soothingly my face and my hands. She took my gloves

135

off and cradled the palm of my hand to her cheek. Then she let it slide off her knees, but without letting it go. She brought her face close to mine and asked:

'Are you brave?'

'I am,' I answered with conviction.

The Girl slowly raised my hand to her mouth and suddenly bit it. I gritted my teeth. She held the bite with an increasing force. I put my other arm around the Girl and started playing with her hair to divert my attention from the pain. She didn't react. At last she let go. I raised my wet, teeth-marked hand to my eyes. The Girl leapt and fell on her bed, tucking herself tightly in her coat.

'Watch the fire,' she called out, turned her back and almost instantly fell asleep.

I was hit by a wave of weariness too. With great effort I pulled up the sleeve of my coat to check the time. It was three in the morning. I thought of fighting the sleep with a cigarette but the matches were wet and I had no strength to move closer to the fire. I just fixed my eyes on it, firmly resolved to stick it out like this till dawn. But the Girl's presence bothered me. I stretched out my hand and felt for her. I found a soft tress of hair and cold smooth forehead. The Girl twitched and turned around. I felt embarrassed. Our agreement was that I was supposed to watch the fire. I turned my eyes back to the fire with renewed zeal. Another gale swept over the trees. Our little hut was getting warmer. I was boiling. Once more I tried to unbutton my coat but then gave up, suddenly worried I might catch a cold. I raised myself a little and immediately crumpled like a rag doll. My eyes shut automatically, against my will.

In the morning I was woken up by the intense cold, as if I had slept outside all night. Effortlessly I leapt to my feet. The Girl, dressed and ready to go, was smothering the fire with snow. All around us lay scattered small, broken branches: the remnants – as I suspected – of our little hut. I stood forlorn and cold. I felt ashamed before the Girl: of my helplessness and lack of discipline in watching the fire. I didn't look great, I knew that. Without paying any attention to me, the Girl was trampling over the fire; then she bent down and threw handfuls of snow in my face.

'Catch me!' she cried cheerfully and ran off.

I started after her in hot pursuit. We ran among the trees, knocking off the branches pillows of snow, and then down a road. At last the Girl stopped, looked at me, and burst out laughing.

'You fell asleep last night. The fire would have gone out if I hadn't woken up in time,' she said. 'But that's OK.'

The last sentence she pronounced softly, but firmly. I stretched out my arm automatically. She took my hand and pulled me after her. We walked fast through a silent misty wood.

'There is no point in looking for a bus,' said the Girl. 'My house is not far from here. I'm a suburban girl. We'll go to my place and have a cup of tea. We should be there in an hour.'

The wood began to grow thinner until it thinned out into copses, which I remembered from my own walks. Then on the horizon loomed the panorama of Our Town. We came out into an open space. Having passed a dirty village with huddled houses, still asleep, we turned into a side road and after a while stopped before a big rusty gate. The Girl unhooked the chain and we entered a wildly overgrown, neglected park. Next to the gate, among the trees, stood a long yellow building, which looked like a warehouse or a coach house, but empty. Further on, along the alley we came to some concrete foundations and an empty lido. Then again thick shrubs, covering almost completely the narrow path under our feet. Finally we stopped before a barricade of empty, rusting cages. This heap of scrap was woven through with branches of trees; in the summer it must have created an impenetrable, iron-green fortification. The Girl pulled me again and we went inside a huge concrete duct, about two metres high.

After a few echoing steps we came out on the other side of

the barricade. From the back it didn't look so fierce. Straight away my eye spied in the heap of brittle old iron a few weak spots through which one could easily sneak back onto the other side. We walked on among empty pens, cages and concrete ditches. When we passed a low hedge it was clear we were in a zoo. At first glance it didn't look much different from the junkyard we'd just passed. The animals sat inside their boxes, the floors of their cages covered with piles of snow. Only an old vulture flapped his wings in the nearest cage, and above a palisade hovered the black silhouette of a doe. I remembered that I had once been in a zoo at this hour and wanted to tell the Girl, but as soon as I opened my mouth she shook her head sternly and silenced me. She took me by the hand and whispered into my ear:

'Come. I'll show you something.'

I nodded, obediently refraining from saying anything. The Girl slowed down. We walked carefully and in silence; only her grip on my hand grew stronger. I couldn't understand why we were creeping like this, for that was the only way I could describe it, but I crept as best I could, holding my breath and trying to put my feet down without making any sound. When we got to a big hut, the Girl motioned me to hide behind a tree trunk. Leaning out from behind the tree our faces were practically touching the wire fence of the cage.

Inside the cage, huge like a gym hall, on a concrete shelf made into a rock, two lynxes copulated. They were doing it softly, gracefully and soundlessly, without purring. It went on for an embarrassingly long time, and in silence. It began to get on my nerves. I felt I could not articulate any kind of reaction to this phenomenon, fundamentally indifferent to me and outside my direct sensual experience yet totally absorbing. I looked at the Girl. Her face was calm and beautiful as usual. She was watching it with concentration, which made her forehead slightly furrowed. Her lips were gently pursed in a kind of smirk, neither contemptuous nor ironic. The aroused

138

animals began to moan and purr. It was unbearable. I tried to wrench myself free and cover my eyes with my hand. But the Girl would not let go, her grip growing stronger still, her fingernail sinking into my hand. Only thanks to my thick gloves she did not draw blood.

'Let go,' I hissed with my throat tight. 'Let go, now! I've had enough. It's stupid . . .'

I was flailing madly behind the tree, unable to pull free. After a while I realised the Girl was no longer holding my hand; I was simply rooted to the spot. The lynxes' moans were growing louder and louder, reaching a pitch of beastly whining. I leaned against the other side of the trunk and with my eyes shut waited through the feline orgasm. After another minute I decided to open my eyes. I was struck by the stillness of the surroundings. My writhing and flailing of a few moments before seemed utterly out of place now as I stood in the midst of a silent snowy landscape. The lynxes lay on their bellies, scratching each other lazily. The female lay with her hind legs stretched out like a woman's legs. A bird swayed a branch above my head and a single black leaf fell on the ground nearby. I turned around, looking for the Girl, but she wasn't there. I wanted to call her but remembered that I didn't even know her name. I walked around the cage, checking behind other trees; the Girl was gone. I got angry: what would be the point of looking for her anyway?

I checked the time. Ten o'clock. I decided to take the shortest route back to town. But as soon as I turned towards the alley I saw her, waiting for me.

12

The following morning before dawn I threw my skis over the shoulder and headed for the zoo. In fact I hadn't arranged to meet the Girl but I was hurrying as if late for a date. The workers gathered in groups at the bus stops looked at me gravely, even hard-heartedly. I didn't have the time, or the patience, to explain to them that the necessity forcing me to take a ride to the woods at this time of day was just as unforgiving as that making them hurry to the cigarette factory. Having passed the bus stop, I fastened the skis on and set off across the empty fields.

The grey skies made the snow glisten with a turbid sheen, which was hard on the eyes. The first part of the run, passing houses and cowsheds, was in fact unpleasant and now and again I was asking myself if I shouldn't go back. How would I justify to the Girl such an early call? Once inside the wood I began to enjoy the run, and the freedom. Sliding along the downy paths, past the tangled black mass of shrubs and bushes, here and there I would knock off a thick snowy hat from a fir branch, giving hushed cries of delight as I went along. I didn't let myself get carried away, constantly reminding myself I had to make it on time for the feline heat.

I entered the zoo through the main gate. I expected the Girl to be waiting for me there and was rather disappointed when she wasn't. I walked slowly along the alley. The animals watched me without any fear in their eyes. The bears stood up on their hind paws and had a closer look at me, but didn't turn their heads when I disappeared from their sight. A young lion ran away at first and then stopped with his paw in mid-air, above a still quivering wooden ball. I turned back and started towards the mouflons' pen, behind which stood the black hut of the caretaker. The hut looked as if someone had just swept the snow in front of the gate, locked the door, bolted the shatters and left for somewhere far away. I stood before it for a long while, hesitating whether I should knock on the shutters or not, but in the end I lacked the courage. I turned back onto the main alley and began to move towards the other entrance, the one we used before. But I couldn't find the way. I had no idea which end of the park was the lynxes' cage, which could serve as my orientation point.

Sliding along on my skis, I came across a long wooden building. Because I was feeling a little cold, I unfastened the skis and went in through the half-open door. The inside of the building was like an elongated, over-wide corridor. Along the walls stood cages with small parrots, hummingbirds and white-footed voles. The stench was overpowering. I lit up a cigarette and moved towards the other end of the corridor, where I saw an open window. It wasn't, as I expected, looking outside, but belonged to a small room, with a floor covered by layers of cotton wool and a small, closed and barred window. In the middle of the floor sat a big monkey wearing a black waistcoat. The animal held some kind of a magazine and was leafing through it with great concentration. After a while the monkey put away the magazine and pulled out from its waistcoat pocket a sheaf of loose pages. I managed to catch a glance at the magazine's cover; it was an old German satirical weekly.

Meanwhile the monkey spread out on the floor the pieces of paper like someone dealing for a game of patience, except that the cards were uniformly blank. He twitched the specs on his nose, though in fact they were just a wire frame without lenses, and sank into thought over his cards, as if trying to decide which to choose. Then, with a quick, thieving swipe, he snatched one of them from the middle row and, having moved to the window, raised it against the light. As far as I could tell from the distance, the watermark on the paper was an erotic picture, drawn in a vulgar and naturalistic way. The monkey examined the paper at length, nodding his head with appreciation, then picked out another one and again looked at it for a long while. At the third, monkey's breast heaved with a soft sigh. At the fourth it glanced quickly, as if not interested, and immediately reached greedily for the next. I had had enough.

I stamped my foot loudly and cried: 'Shoo!' The monkey froze with a card in his hand, turning his eyes on me with a tense, painful look. Suddenly he leapt in the air, jumped onto

141

a ledge above the window, and just in front of my nose a metal curtain descended. Without thinking I started pummelling it with my fists. The inside of the room was totally silent; instead, the parrots raised a deafening racket, their cries piercing my ears like steel shavings. The baboons and chimpanzees began thrashing about in their cages.

Tormented, I ran out of the building, slamming the door behind me. My skis were waiting for me on the snow, familiar and friendly. I fastened them on and threw myself into a run across the park. Suddenly, as I reached the main alley, the silence was rent by a hoarse, guttural shriek. I recognised the lynxes' call of love. Automatically I turned in that direction. The noises grew more frequent; the intercourse must have been reaching the climax. I ran as fast as I could. At last, in the perspective of empty pens and barred enclosures, I saw the lynxes' cage. The Girl stood outside the caretaker's hut, pale, with eyes shut. Her face was sombre, pained. I ran up to her and grabbed her in my arms. We fell on the snow. The Girl was kissing me feverishly and passionately, not possessively as before, but submissively, like a woman. The skis, still fastened to my feet, splayed widely, drawing on the snow long tangled spirals.

When we got up the Girl immediately returned to her previous role. She helped me to get the snow off and in a dry, matter-of-fact tone of voice she observed I was cold and that in view of this she wanted to invite me for a cup of tea. The caretaker's house was not abandoned as I thought. We sat on the edge of a plush, richly tasselled sofa and drank our tea in silence. Apart from the sofa the room didn't contain any other furniture. The kitchen, however, was crammed with chairs, a long ungainly table and a sideboard.

'My father,' said the Girl, 'is of the opinion that I can receive guests only when the room has all the furniture. That is: table, armchairs, linen cupboard and a clock. He thinks that now it would be improper to bring people in here. But I love you.'

The Girl slurped her tea and we fell back into silence. I looked around the room and suddenly noticed a white piece of paper lying on the varnished floor, the same kind as those looked at by the monkey. I decided to pay it no attention, but the paper seemed to have filled the whole room and drew my eyes to itself with a magnetic force. I was trying to concentrate on the Girl's profile and her hands but my eyes, even when wholly focused on her figure, slipped down onto the floor and secretly sought out the accursed piece of paper. The Girl sat slumped, saying nothing and sipping her tea, of which she seemed to have prepared copious quantities for the two of us. I turned my eyes to the window but somehow the card still remained within my field of vision. The Girl picked up my hand lightly. I reciprocated with a gentle squeeze but rather mechanically. The presence of that card embarrassed me.

'Let's kiss,' offered the Girl.

We began to kiss, but we were not enjoying it. Our kisses were cold and clumsy. Only now did I realise that the Girl had simply no idea how to kiss, as if she had never kissed in her life. We lay next to each other.

'We love each other,' said the Girl indifferently.

'I love you and you love me,' I confirmed, kissing her gently on the cheek. I fell into musing about our few common experiences. I told her about our little fir hut deep in the forest. The Girl was listening quietly and when I fell silent she said:

'We built the little fir hut in five minutes. It's all nonsense. The little hut you were talking about is impossible, isn't it? My big, silly boy. You believed in a fir hut . . .'

I wanted to protest but she calmed me down with a touch. The sound of a bell came from behind the window; with it came the sound of animals from all corners of the zoo. The Girl jumped off the sofa.

'Father is about to start feeding the animals. Come with me, you have to see that.'

The Girl bent down and picked up the white card from the

floor. She crumpled it quickly in her hand, then tore it into little shreds and threw it into the kitchen.

'I've had enough of this filth,' she sighed. The bell whose ring got us out of the empty room was fixed to the shaft of a cart drawn by a donkey. By the cart's side walked a small man wrapped in a long black sheepskin and a big hat.

'We have a guest today,' called out the Girl. 'I wanted to show him the feeding. You will start with the predators, won't you? Great. I knew the predators were first.'

The Father was not answering but the Girl kept talking, answering her own questions, laughing and teasing him. The father stopped the cart in front of the low long shed and carried out of it a basket filled with chopped-up meat and bones. His face was so swaddled in his collar, scarf and hat that I could not see his features. They didn't seem to be that interesting anyway; the face was flat and unshaven. The father went back once more and brought out a second load of meat. When he came out for the third time he was carrying my auntie's corpse. From the first glance I had no doubt it was the very same corpse. Its limbs were cut off at the knees and elbows, the head chopped off with an axe. The Father put the naked corpse on the cart and we moved on. The Girl squeezed my hand and whispered into my ear:

'We'll be feeding our cats, you know. Our wonderful lynxes.'

I nodded my head automatically and lightly brushed my lips on her head. We toured the whole zoo, stopping in front of the predators' cages. All that time I observed the naked torso trembling on the cart's trellis, making sure it indeed belonged to my killed auntie. There seemed to be no doubt. The torso bore all the familiar marks: the signs of my victories and defeats, and on its side I even recognised the holes eaten out by Aunt Emilia and Granny. At last we got rid of all of the feed, except for the corpse which remained alone in the cart.

We were approaching the lynxes' cage. Despite a certain

embarrassment I felt joy. Now, the nightmare of so many days was about to disappear down the lynxes' throats. I thought: here I was, accompanying my aunt on her last passage, and I felt sorry that I might be saying goodbye to the corpse, to all that struggle, which cost me so much effort and energy. The Father, as if eavesdropping on my thoughts and hearing the word 'funeral', took his hat off and followed the cart bareheaded. The Girl let go of my hand and lowered her head. Crows cawed among the treetops.

The lynxes, furry and excited, their eyes burning with healthy appetite, crowded at the bars. The Father raised the metal trap door at the bottom of the cage and slid in the torso. The animals began to eat. We watched how quickly and skilfully they were dealing with the awkward body, how before our eyes the corpse was changing and losing its form. When the female ate her way through the side bearing the marks of my old girls' teeth – I sighed a sigh of relief. The corpse lost its attributes, it had been stripped off its personality. Finally on the cage's floor there was just a heap of bones. The Father unbuttoned his sheepskin, pulled out a packet of cigarettes and offered me one. I looked into his eyes and recognised them; he winked at me discreetly. His waistcoat was red. The Girl cuddled up to me and put her arm around me.

We became a family.

13

Auntie returned from her sanatorium warm and tanned. She wrapped herself around my neck and kissed me on both cheeks. I felt a little awkward with her. I was at a loss how to explain to her the presence of her corpse in the bathtub, and then I was a little thrown by her new shawl and beret, and different buttons on the familiar coat. A long absence always creates that sort of distance. But Auntie was practical and good-natured, as usual.

'I haven't seen you for so long.' She was speaking fast. 'How have you been getting on, my boy? I bet the flat is a tip, God have mercy on me. Why haven't you written? I was beginning to get worried, believe it or not. Have you been attending the lectures? I presume the flat is just as I left it.'

Weighed down by Auntie's bag I walked alongside her, smiling. I wasn't even trying to answer any of her questions, as I knew she wouldn't give me time to form a sentence. Auntie took me under my arm and chattered away.

'Shall we take a taxi? But I see all are taken. We'll take a drozhka, or let's go on foot. Such wonderful sunshine. Let's run.'

Holding me fast by my arm, she broke into a trot. She was running down the pavement, sweeping the passers-by out of her way. Auntie's heavy bag dragged me down, knocking about my knees. I was beginning to run out of breath. I watched Auntie's face, hoping it would soon come out in a sweat and she would be running out of breath too. Nothing of the sort. Auntie was trotting along, splashing mud with her booties. Apparently the sanatorium had done her a lot of good. Before I knew it I was hanging off her arm, shuffling my feet just fast enough to keep my balance.

'How about some coffee?' Auntie screamed into my ear.

We were just approaching a coffee shop. I couldn't answer. I could hardly breathe and my eyes were watering. We burst into the coffee shop like a hurricane. Auntie ordered two coffees and two cakes. Munching forlornly on the cake I listened to her outpouring of words. There was no way I could get a word in edgeways or explain anything. At least I was pleased I didn't have to run with a heavy bag down a muddy street.

The distance from the coffee shop to home we covered at a more reasonable pace. Once inside, Auntie, without taking her coat off, went into the bedroom and sat heavily on the bed. Climbing up the stairs had taken some puff out of her at last. Inside the four walls of our flat I began to see again in her features the old signs of tiredness and age. The moment of rest didn't last long, though. She got up, took off her coat and booties, and began pottering about the flat. I didn't help her with the coat. At this time, my gesture would be irrelevant and meaningless before the decisive moment about to happen. I sprawled on the bed, listening to Auntie making noises in the kitchen. I was waiting.

At last the door to the bathroom squeaked. I got up. I could not resist participating in the most dramatic moment of the whole adventure. Auntie stood over the bath, shaking her head.

'Boy, boy, boy,' she said with reproach, 'why did you bring all these plants here? And how could you clatter the whole bathtub like this? I bet you didn't take a single bath while I was away, did you, you dirty boy. Help me move these plants.'

With some reluctance I began to shift the old araucaria while Auntie picked up the two cacti and we took them back to the room. My little altar ceased to exist. The scraps of the corpse littering the bathtub among the ice were cold and devoid of any charisma. Auntie clutched at her head.

'Jerzy,' she cried, 'what have you been doing here? Get the brush, let's clean it quickly. Pull up your sleeves, you'll get your shirt dirty.'

I got down to cleaning the bathtub. The biggest problem was with the torso which, even though gutted, was still quite heavy. But Auntie helped me. We carried it out onto the kitchen balcony and hung it out on the balustrade.

Just then on the neighbouring balcony Mrs Malinowska was beating her carpets. Seeing Auntie she sent her a radiant smile and the two ladies exchanged courtesies. I took the last remnants out in a bucket and chucked them in the rubbish bin outside.

Auntie poured half a packet of cleaning powder into the bathtub and, armed with brushes, we started scrubbing it clean.

Eleven-year-old in Love

Bawler, cry-baby . . .
Why are you crying?
My sweetheart's gone away
And how old are you?
Eleven . . .
Shame, such a big lad and crying
I never cry, sir
Even when I scrape my knees
And I can take the cane without batting an eyelid
Only today my heart aches
You are too young for heartaches
I know, sir
You are too big to cry
And too small to love
So I wander the earth
With holes in my tights
And big red ears